The Riches of the Poor

George Mikes has written . . .

GEORGE MIKES

THE RICHES
OF THE POOR

Who's Who

———————

A journey round the
World Health Organisation

'O health! health! The blessing of the
rich! The riches of the poor! Who can buy
thee at too dear a rate, since there is no
enjoying this world without thee.'
Ben Jonson, *Volpone*

ANDRE DEUTSCH

First published 1987 by
André Deutsch Limited
105-106 Great Russell Street WC1B 3JJ

ISBN 0 233 98138 1

Printed in Great Britain by
Ebenezer Baylis & Son Ltd Worcester

Contents

———◆———

Introduction

A friend of mine telephoned from the Continent and told me that smallpox had been completely eradicated. 'Good news,' I replied. He added that smallpox was the one and only disease that had been so completely defeated. I asked him to convey my thanks and congratulations to all concerned and meant to put the receiver down. My friend went on to say that the people largely responsible for the total defeat of smallpox were WHO, the World Health Organisation, and he was 'phoning me because they wanted me to write a book on the subject. There must be some misunderstanding, I told him. Perhaps they saw in some reference book that I am entitled to call myself Dr (which, nevertheless, I have never done). I am a Doctor of Law, not of Medicine. Doctors of Law know very little about smallpox and I know even less than most.

No, no, my friend reassured me, they did not expect me to write a medical or scientific book on the eradication of smallpox, but a humorous one. I was a little surprised but saw their point. If an outbreak of smallpox is a tragic event then its disappearance is a joyous one.

The whole conversation was so ludicrous that I decided that if it wasn't a misunderstanding it must be a hoax. On the other hand, my friend is an intelligent and reliable man and, I felt, he was simply conveying a message as he understood – or perhaps misunderstood – it.

The next time I visited Geneva I talked to people at WHO and, of course, they did not have a side-splitting

1

book on smallpox in mind. They asked me if I would be ready to write a book on health in general; a book in the style of my other books. If I was prepared to do that they would be at my disposal and would help in my researches.

I said I had to think it over. I kept thinking about this utterly unexpected idea – which I should never have produced by myself – and the more I thought the more it appealed to me. My answer to WHO was an eager Yes and the result is this book in the Reader's hand.

I must make it clear, however, that while I am grateful to WHO for their help and the facilities they offered me, this is my book not theirs. For all the views expressed in it, for all the remarks made, I am fully responsible and only I am to be blamed.

PART ONE

Fairly Strictly Personal

Health and Me

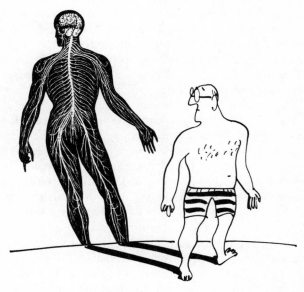

A few years ago I was filling up my car with petrol when another customer at the filling station shouted a friendly 'Hello!' to me. I reciprocated his greeting with the warmth reserved for people I fail to recognise. But he was not taken in: 'You have no idea who I am,' he said. 'No, I haven't,' I admitted in a manly fashion. 'You are a lucky devil. I am your doctor.'

I mentioned this encounter to one of my tennis partners and he asked me when, in fact, I had last seen my doctor. In 1977 I damaged my eye with a tennis ball and then I went to see my doctor's partner who sent me on to a specialist. Prior to that I saw the doctor himself perhaps ten years before when I needed a US visa and had to be inoculated against that then still uneradicated illness, smallpox. Before *that* I had never seen him.

Then I asked my friend: 'When did *you* last see your

doctor?' He replied without hesitation: 'June 1938.'

Not long after this conversation, the same friend called me an hour before we were due to play tennis and told me that he was feeling dizzy, so could I find someone else to make up the four. I managed to replace him, and when reporting the reason for his absence, I remarked: 'Come to think of it, this is the first time in sixteen years that any of us has cried off because of health reasons.' 'That is not so,' said another tennis partner, a retired Colonel, then just over eighty and now eighty-four. 'You were away for a month, once, with tennis elbow, and then for about six months because of your eye; and while you were away John cancelled a game for the same reason as today. There is in fact only one of us who has never called off a game because of health reasons.'

He didn't have to say who that was. But he added: 'Not even when I had a stroke.'

I looked at him with surprise, but obviously he was not inclined to add anything. Three days later I met his wife at a party and she confirmed his story. For the first time in their long married life she had left him alone for a few days, and just after her departure, on a Friday, the Colonel had a slight stroke. On Saturday he was back on the tennis court. He explained to his wife, on her return, that he had not called the doctor because he did not want to be put to bed, treated like an invalid and – most important – forbidden to play tennis. The Colonel still plays very good tennis today, and has never missed a game since his stroke.*

---

*On a beautiful spring day, between my writing that paragraph and finishing this book, we were playing our usual Thursday afternoon game. Suddenly the Colonel said 'I'm sorry, but I don't feel too well.' Then he died. Several times he had told us that he would like to die on the tennis court, his dream being to do so after serving an ace. Unfortunately, when it happened he had just served a double fault. Well – we can't have quite everything in life, nor even in death.

Apart from the matter of missing or not missing a few tennis games, I have never given much thought to questions of health. I thought the reason was simple: I was lucky with my own health so, naturally enough, I failed to develop a great interest in the subject. It took this book to force me to face facts. It is not quite as straightforward as that. I was trying to run away from something very important, without realising throughout a lifetime what I was doing.

But before coming to this, I must make a few preliminary remarks.

First, although I avoid doctors whenever I can, I do have some health problems. For about thirty years I have had a hiatus hernia. It is not painful and does not trouble me too much, but it is a nuisance. When I eat fast or swallow something tough or talk too much while eating I get the hiccups. It usually goes away after a few minutes but sometimes it lasts longer. In the past it often lasted much longer – thirty-six hours on one occasion. This is not at all funny although quite a few people find it amusing. A friend of mine, a woman doctor, insisted that I had to see a specialist and sent me to (she said) the greatest living expert on hiatus hernia. Before going to him, I looked him up in *Who's Who* and noticed that we were nearly contemporaries; he being, if I remember correctly, just a few weeks younger than I. He put up the X-ray pictures on a string and explained my trouble to me with brilliant clarity. For the first time in my life I understood what was wrong with me. Well, what was to be done? 'Nothing,' he said. 'You get the hiccups when you eat fast, swallow tough bits and talk while eating. Consequently, eat slowly, eat tender food and don't talk while eating.' This sounded very reasonable but the kind of thing any person with a little common sense might have told me. 'Well,' I said with perhaps a slight disappointment in my voice, 'they say you are the greatest expert in the world...' He interrupted me. 'Be that as it may. Perhaps I am, perhaps I am not. But I am nearly exactly your age, and as it happens – a curious coincidence – I have had the same trouble for exactly the same time as you. I would not dream of having an operation or sending you to have one. The operation in itself is quite simple, but getting to the required spot can be a real problem. Forget about an operation. You just live with it.' I was only too eager to forget about an operation and have been living with my trouble ever since. I am a very bad hypochondriac and keep forgetting my instructions: I still eat fast, I still talk too much, I still swallow tough chunks, so the hiccups still come. But then they go away.

Then, as I am becoming an old boy, I have to get up during the night, often several times, to visit the loo – but this is no more than an inconvenience. I go back to bed and I am asleep again as soon as I put my head down on the pillow.

The last time when I was really treated by a doctor was in 1957. I spent a few months in Rome, writing a film script, and I caught jaundice. It came out on my arrival home and I spent a week in bed. That was the last time I was ill and, apart from that one week, I have not been ill in bed since the age of eleven or so with one single exception, when I nearly died.

As a young journalist I got blood poisoning. When my colleagues from the paper rang the nursing home, they were told that all hope had to be abandoned, so my paper published a warm and very flattering obituary. Meanwhile, however, I was given a blood transfusion which performed wonders. As the blood flowed into my veins I started feeling better, and next morning, I read my obituary and was truly cheered up. Later I had the feeling that my Editor was annoyed. He hated any inaccuracy and felt that I had let the paper down by recovering.

As a child I went through all the illnesses one can find

in the book: whooping cough was nothing to speak about but at the age of two I nearly died of scarlet fever and at the age of seven of dysentery. But – apart from the two instances mentioned – I had no troubles after the age of eleven. I never had influenza, never had a really incapacitating common cold, never had an operation – not even a tiny one. I don't have headaches. I eat what I like, I drink very little alcohol (by choice) but have a strong black coffee after meals – including dinner – and sleep like a baby.

I know, of course, that all this means absolutely nothing as far as the future is concerned. I may collapse and die tomorrow. If I do not die tomorrow, I shall die on another day, like everybody else, and I do not resent the fact. I fail to understand humanity's (with a few exceptions) abject fear of death. When someone has eaten a lot, he does not want more food; when he has slept enough, he does not want a rest. Why is it that so few people feel that they have *lived enough?* Why do they not say: 'It was pleasant, most enjoyable, but enough is enough?' Can they not see that there is nothing wrong in leaving this earth after a full and reasonably happy life? And why do people mislead themselves with stories of an eternal afterlife which, to my mind, is utter rubbish. When I die, I shall be dead and gone and may, perhaps, survive a few extra years in the memory of those few people who loved or at least liked me. To live on in the hearts of good friends is – for me – a pleasanter prospect than heaven, with all those angels playing their boring harps – often, I'm sure, out of tune. So, whether I die tomorrow or have a few more years to live, I am fully aware that I have been lucky to have gone through these last sixty years without any health troubles worth complaining about.

I have always felt deep sympathy for those whose health was fragile or worse. For a long time I attributed these sentiments to my noble character, but then psychological insight intervened. Psychology is the science which teaches us that all our noble feelings are, in fact, inspired by base instinct. The truth must be that I am afraid of illness and what I really want to do is to run away from all its manifestations. When something is wrong with me, my reaction, on the surface, is not fear or anxiety but anger. I get angry with the machinery of my body as I get angry with the machinery of a motor car when it lets me down. I kick my car when it fails to perform properly (not only in anger – I have found that a kick may mend many minor faults), and I am inclined to kick myself when not feeling a hundred per cent well. When someone complains to me about his (and that always means in this text *her* as well) ill-health or fatigue, or misses an appointment because he does not feel well, my first reaction is impatience and irritation. I have to tell myself in most emphatic terms that this is the attitude of a barbarian; one should feel sympathy and show understanding, so that is what I compel myself to do. Malingerers and hypochondriacs do not deserve much sympathy, of course, but who am I to tell the genuine from the phony?

Illness, then, as personal experience goes, is something of a strange territory for me. I am so ignorant about the functioning of the human body that not long ago I had to ask a doctor friend about the role of the liver. I could not recall what the liver was for. My doctor friend was outraged because 'one cannot live without the liver'. 'That's quite irrelevant,' I replied. 'I cannot live without X either, still I have no idea how *she* functions.'

Recently, however, when I started thinking about this book, some long-forgotten memories came slowly back to me which explain a great deal about my real motives.

My father was a lawyer in the country in Hungary. He died when I was ten years old. My stepfather was a doctor with a vast and flourishing practice in Budapest. It was his natural desire that I should study medicine

10

and, in due course, take over his practice. I absolutely and firmly refused. I did not want anything to do with medicine. This was strange. I had never witnessed any horrifying scenes or seen dreadfully sick, suffering patients; in addition, my stepfather quite naturally had many doctor and surgeon friends and I was very fond of nearly all of them. A number of my close relations, whom I loved, were also doctors and my sister, whom I loved most, was determined to become one. Yet, my resistance to the idea was fierce. So I went and studied law instead, as my real father had done. Later I heard that my father had gone through more or less the same experience. He did become a medical student but anatomy lessons made him sick – sitting down to munch sandwiches amid dismembered corpses, a severed limb here, another there – he just could not bear it and after one single semester changed over to the law. Had I known this earlier, I should have been convinced that I was simply emulating my father. As I heard it later, I just felt proud of sharing his revulsion.

All this brings me nearer to my real and carefully concealed reasons for hating all things medical, but the truth – as is its habit – cuts deeper.

The Culprit: One Doctor

Just a few days ago I gave an interview to Irish Radio. The subject was my book, *How to be Poor*, which had just been published as a paperback in Penguin. The interviewer asked me why I hated doctors so much. 'Oh no,' I replied, 'I don't hate them at all.' At first I had no idea what he was talking about but he pressed on. 'You have a chapter on Professional Deformities...' I interrupted: 'Oh that! There I simply describe how certain professions create certain deformities. Judges become semi-divine, teachers like to surround themselves with children who are inferior to them in knowledge, doctors love to play the role of Know-Alls and are inclined to keep the patient's secrets from the patient himself and...' The interviewer interrupted me, quite firmly: 'I know all that. You mention other professions, that's quite true. But you *do* hate doctors.'

I was surprised and shocked that I had made this impression on a reader, a perfectly neutral stranger. Well, *do* I hate doctors?

It suddenly all came back in a flash. Memories I had buried for long decades. Events of which I had not consciously thought for almost sixty years.

At the age of fourteen I spent a pleasant summer holiday with my brother Tibor and cousin Hédy at Hédy's aunt's place in Transylvania. My hosts were not close relations – I think I had never seen them before – but they were kind people and it never occurred to me to ponder the question: why were we, Tibor and I, suddenly invited to spend a summer holiday with them? I went to a boy-scouts' camp with one of my hosts' sons and enjoyed myself immensely.

My father had died three years earlier. My mother moved up from Southern Hungary to Budapest, to her parents, while I stayed in the southern city of Pécs to continue my studies (we called my school a *gymnasium*).My mother had a sister called Violet who had married a doctor called Dezsö Halmos. My cousin Hédy was their child. My aunt Violet died when Hédy was born and Hédy was being brought up by all sorts of relations, among them the aunt who was our host this summer. In Budapest in the meantime her father, Dr Halmos, had his surgery in my grandparents' large flat where my mother lived. Naturally enough, my mother and Halmos – two lonely people – spent a lot of time together. They fell in love and decided to marry.

I was completely unaware of all these developments. I might have suspected something if I had lived in Budapest; but I lived in faraway Pécs.

Now, at the end of our holiday, my uncle Dezsö Halmos came down to pick us up. He came with my mother, which surprised me. He called me aside and informed me, rather solemnly, that he was going to marry my mother. Everybody congratulated them and

13

even me. Everybody told me what a lucky boy I was. Having lost a father, now I was gaining my uncle as a new father. Indeed, I was lucky. But I failed to appreciate my great luck. I was aware of a tremendous shock but not of tremendous luck. This man is going to go to bed with my mother, if he has not done so already. I had just reached the most sensitive Oedipal age of adolescence and was deeply disturbed by this thought. How does this man *dare* to touch my beautiful mother? I dismissed the idea that they were having an affair. No, my mother was not that type of person. But what was yet to come was unbearable. Yet, I had to grin and bear it and accept everybody's sincere congratulations on this disaster.

My stepfather was always very good to me. There was a famous story in Hungary about the brilliant and witty writer Frigyes Karinthy. He married a woman doctor, Aranka Boehm. Both of them had been married before and each of them brought a son into the new set-up. Then they produced a third son. One day they heard a terrific din from the nursery and Aranka asked her husband to go and see what was going on. Karinthy returned and reported: 'Oh, it's nothing serious. Only your son and my son are beating up our son.'

Nothing similar ever occurred in our house. We did not beat each other up and there was absolutely no discrimination between my mother's two sons and my stepfather's daughter. I love my brother but did not love my new sister any less. I was always fully aware of the fact that my own father could not have been more devoted to me than my stepfather was. Yet – he was an altogether different proposition. On a conscious level I am grateful to him; for his generosity, his love, even his strictness – which was not unmixed with a dash of sadism. I did not confess even to myself that I did not really love him. I called him 'Father' but I nearly choked on the word, I could never utter it naturally. He had his faults – who hasn't? But his so-called 'faults' have nothing to do with the fact that I rejected him in my heart. His unforgivable crime was that he made love to my mother.

Had he married her when I was four I wouldn't have cared a damn; had they married when I was twenty-four I would have been delighted. But as they married when I was fourteen, I could never forgive him; or the medical profession.

The Secret of Eternal Youth, and Things Like That

Man is the only animal who (or which) cannot face reality. Other animals accept things as they come: when a fox is wounded, he tries to lick his wound and sometimes he will get better. When he is torn to bits by hounds, he dies. But foxes have no fancy ideas about afterlife. Elephants do not invent theories about the migration of the soul (maybe they know from the Bible that they have no souls, although if there existed an elephant-Bible, it would certainly teach them that *only* elephants have souls). The platypus knows nothing about heaven and hell. Chimpanzees do not believe in resurrection. Man does all this, not because he is all that special an animal but because he cannot face the plain fact that he is born, he lives and he dies and then disappears from this planet for good – just like foxes, elephants, platypuses and chimpanzees.

Ever since Man started jotting down his history and ideas (i.e. for a very short while) he has been chasing other utopias, too. His capacity for self-deception, and his ability to fool his fellow-men, are astonishing. Man has always dreamed of worlds which could not exist: a world without disease, without old age; a world of eternal youth. Luckily for him – for all of us – these dreams have remained and must remain dreams. If we achieved eternal life, if all men who have ever lived were alive today, or were resurrected, that would indeed be a disaster compared with which the Great Plague, the Inquisition, the famines of China and Ethiopia and all the wars of history (including Hiroshima and Nagasaki) would count as minor inconveniences. Yet, instead of being delighted that eternal life and eternal youth cannot be achieved, man goes on longing for these horrors.

The first written evidence of this self-deception comes from the fourth century BC. A medical treatise of that period explains that 'in ancient times' (the writer having no idea that *he* was living in ancient times, just as we have no idea that we, too, live in ancient times) people lived to be a hundred years old, yet remained vigorous, active and in perfect health.

In my youth there existed a belated prophet of ever-lasting youth and eternal good health by the name of Bicsérdy. He was a Hungarian who lived in Transylvania, that part of Hungary which was given to Romania after World War I. Bicsérdism became a tremendous fad, the man had hundreds of thousands of followers. In fact, Bicsérdism, for a while, was not just a fad but a universal craze. According to Bicsérdy you had to get up at four o'clock in the morning, run around barefoot in the dewy grass of your garden or a park for an hour or so, and then eat raw carrots all day and nothing else at all. If you did that, you would live for ever. I visited Transylvania when I was a young man but did not become a convert, in spite of the most ardent pressure. I felt that if I had to get up at four a.m. every dawn and live on raw carrots for the rest of my life, then I did not wish even to reach a ripe old age; indeed, I'd rather die today. Bicsérdy, poor thing, caught a terrible cold during one of his dawn runs in the dew and died at the early age of forty. *Requiescat in pace*. It all shows that life is cruelly unjust. I am still here, fifty years on, one of the few to remember him although I have never touched a raw carrot since the day of his death.

Various nations and communities respond to the problem in various ways. In Stalin's Russia old age – like everything else – became a political issue. People were fed on stories about the longevity of the Georgian people. In Georgia humanity was stronger, healthier and lived much longer than anywhere else. People – we were told – played football at the age of 150 and easily beat other (non-Georgian) teams consisting of teenagers. After the match they went home, had an enormous meal and made love to their wives (ladies of 145 or so). Their sons – youths of 125 – respected and obeyed their fathers. All this rubbish was sheer sycophancy. Stalin was a Georgian and these stories were invented to reassure him that he was immortal.

Rousseau's solution was the Noble Savage. France and the whole civilised world of his age caught the bug, but luckily the craze for the Noble Savage died before humanity could revert to cave-dwelling and crawling on all fours.

In present-day America good health is deemed to be a matter of money. 'Good health is purchasable,' declared an American sage (who tried to sell it). The United States is the richest nation in the world and – they maintain – that's why its people are the healthiest. Except that they are not. The life expectancy of an American over forty-five is hardly greater than it was at

18

the turn of the century and less than the life expectancy of many poorer nations. 'He [the American] claims the highest standard of living in the world but ten per cent of his income must go for accommodating the sick' – writes René Dubos in his *Mirage of Health* (Allen & Unwin, 1960). The Americans believe in wonder-drugs to cure heart diseases, cancer, diseases of the liver and so on, but do very little to lead a life which would prevent these ills from developing. The Americans laugh louder than the rest of humanity and their characteristic happy and confident smile has become a national disease itself. 'But,' goes on Dubos, 'one out of every four citizens will have to spend at least some months or years in a mental asylum. One may wonder indeed whether the pretence of superior health is not itself rapidly becoming a mental aberration.'

A very different approach has been developed by a close friend of mine whom I shall call Peter. He is in his seventy-sixth year and is a high official in a small country, still as active as ever. He travels a lot and after arriving, having completed an eighteen-hour journey – including all-night travel – while his younger assistants faint with jet-lag, he sits down to negotiate complicated treaties and outwits all the locals who have spent the previous night in their comfortable beds. 'What is your secret?' people ask him. 'It is very simple,' he replies. 'I have always eaten much more than it is good for me. My diet consists mostly of animal fats, plenty of cholesterol, salt and sugar. I have always taken the greatest care to remain overweight. I do like my wine and brandy and – this is extremely important – I have never taken any exercise.'

I repeated this attractive recipe for eternal youth to a doctor friend. She was not impressed. 'Yes,' she said, 'it *is* possible for a man to get safely across a busy motorway, blindfolded. It *can* happen. Yet, doing it blindfolded is not to be recommended as the secret of safely crossing motorways.'

19

Winston Churchill agreed, at least to some extent, with Peter. He declared: 'Whenever I have the urge to exercise, I lie down and refuse to get up until the urge has gone.'

An old story throws some beneficial light on this question.

In a home full of very ancient and pretty helpless geriatrics, there is one man who is a shade sprightlier than the rest. He helps the old gentlemen up and down stairs, carries chairs for them, holds the door open while they totter through. Everybody likes him, everybody is impressed by him. Someone asks him: 'Tell us, what is the secret of your wonderful condition? What sort of diet did you keep?'

'Diet? I have been eating like a horse all my life. And all the wrong things.'

'But you didn't drink?'

'Didn't I? A full bottle of brandy before lunch, every day. And then wine for lunch, wine for dinner and lots of whisky and more brandy until I went to sleep about two or three in the morning.'

'Did you smoke?'

'Like a chimney. Cigarettes mostly. But marihuana, too. That is when I couldn't get hold of coke.'

'But did you abstain from women?'

'I slept with a woman every day. Often with two a day. Sometimes three.'

'Amazing. And how old are you?'

'Twenty-eight.'

PART TWO

WHO'S WHO?

One World? Two Worlds?

A superficial acquaintance with the work of the World Health Organisation is enough to make me realise that my views and remarks are those of a parochial West-European. People should not be ashamed of being West-Europeans, though many of them are. And neither should they be over-proud of it. Western Europe, or 'the West', includes such vast, non-European places as the United States, Australia and New Zealand, but all of them put together are only a small part of the globe, with very different problems from the rest. Humanity belongs to two main groups: the Third World and the First. (I know very little about the Second. It's never mentioned.)

You have never heard of a Ugandan peasant or a Jamaican farm-worker on a banana plantation who does not have enough 'exercise'. They all have more than enough. There are few Indian or Ethiopian villagers threatened by the dangers of over-eating. Their problem

is under-eating. If they have a problem about cholesterol, they need more of it, not less.

That does not mean that we Westerners are necessarily healthier than the people of the Third World. See
previous remarks about Americans who are the weal-
thiest but certainly not the healthiest of all nations.
Africans and Polynesians, and many others, disregard
minor ailments which send us rushing to our doctors who
then keep us in bed for days. If we drank the water some
of these communities keep drinking we would die of
cholera. *They* drink that water with impunity. (One has
heard innumerable stories about concentration camp
victims, during the War – middle-aged and middle-class
people who had caught innumerable colds during their
previous comfortable lives. When their brutal and mon-
strous captors made them stand in the snow almost
naked for hours on end, many of them suffered no
ill-effects.)

This however, is only one side of the picture. The other
side is more discouraging. Once again two different
worlds are staring at each other with incomprehension.

A great many illnesses which have been more or less
eliminated in the West – polio, tetanus, tuberculosis,
whooping cough, measles (smallpox is in a different
chapter) are still widespread killer-diseases in the Third
World. (The Third World is nowadays called the 'Developing Countries'. Some of them *are* developing, others
are not.) The two sides seem to be worlds apart. The
problems of one (overfeeding etc) are the dreams of the
other. We live different lives; we die different deaths.

As we in the West are supposed to be more advanced,
WHO'S task seemed for a short while to be simple. The
Third World must be brought up – up? – to the level of
the First – or as near to it as possible. This simple
concept proved all right, even beneficial, in quite a few
cases; in others it caused trouble and even disaster.

It happened on several occasions that Western missions were horrified to see African or South American tribes living with their animals (either animals sharing people's huts or people sharing animals' stables). They washed in the same water and, sometimes, drank water in which animals had urinated. Yet they remained healthy. As soon as well-intentioned Westerners taught them a bit of hygiene, they started falling ill. Those wonderful Western methods destroyed their health. The moral is *not* that we all should drink water into which buffaloes have urinated.

On the other hand I have heard a few success-stories. This one comes from Thailand. In one district people hardly ever washed because of the shortage of water. WHO taught them how to catch rainwater in reservoirs and how to separate rainwater and drinking water from water suitable for washing clothes and yaks and elephants but for nothing else. These newfangled ideas were received at first with the utmost suspicion, but the Siamese are too intelligent a people not to have been convinced by evidence in front of their eyes. The new system has changed their lives. Lots of diseases disappeared, the community has become altogether healthier. Now that they have enough water in their reservoirs they keep themselves much cleaner and this has improved their health further. Today they are prepared to pay for their water-supply – and that says a lot.

Benefits are not always so obvious as in this case. Most Western newspaper-readers have heard of the problem of powdered milk. African children were introduced to artificial milk and some of them died. The milk was blamed, but the culprits were the dirty water in which it was dissolved and the excreta of flies on the teats: impossible to explain to any mother who has just lost a child, without sounding as though you were blaming her in order to excuse yourself.

Or take vaccination. The practice is often received with resentment. Mothers hate seeing their babies being pricked with those long and menacing needles – and sometimes babies are inocculated only to die afterwards, in spite of it. Perhaps the needles were dirty; perhaps the vaccination came too late; perhaps the baby dies of some illness unconnected with the vaccine. Excuses won't wash. For the mother it was that jab with the horrible needle that killed her child.

It is an old fallacy of the human race that it is enough to show reason for reason to be victorious. One would have expected the experience of the eighteenth-century Rationalists to cure us of this fallacy but this is not the case. African witch-doctors are often more intelligent than Western rationalists. Secretly they administer penicillin to their patients. People, of course, insist on the old hocus-pocus, too, so they get it from the witch-doctor. It is hard to say – as there are so many psychosomatic illnesses – whether the patients are cured by penicillin or by the hocus-pocus.

One meets the equivalent of the witch-doctor in our own society. A very eminent specialist told me once that when he was treating a sick child whose life was in the balance, he had gone to church to pray for his little patient's life. I am an old sceptic and am convinced that the 'supernatural' never helps the patient; but sometimes obviously, it helps the doctor.

The West has absolutely no reason to expect reason on medical matters to prevail among Third World peoples. We all know about Copernicus's fear of the stake, the tribulations of Galileo, the vituperations against Darwin, the horror which greeted Harvey's deviation from Galen's medical bible, and the attempts to oust Pasteur from the medical profession. The list could be extended almost indefinitely. Einstein's theories were received with doubt, Freud's with derision, and great artists (whose laundry lists, written out in their own hands, fetch fortunes today) have starved. So why should people unfamiliar with the principle of vaccination not mistrust the injection needle?

26

That people were reluctant to accept Darwin and Freud is understandable. They undermined humanity's conceit, belief in itself, snobbery, so it would have been comforting if they had been wrong. But even when people are convinced that a teaching or discovery is right, they still resist it. Everybody knows that cigarette smoking – or all smoking – is destructive to health and a potential killer. Yet millions of people – brilliant, advanced Westerners among them – go on smoking, either fooling themselves that smoking will not harm *them,* or dismissing the whole idea as unproven. Indeed, they go much further. Nearly all the armies of the West go on issuing regular cigarette rations to the troops. It is very much in the interest of any army to keep its men and women in good health but, they say, it is even more important to avoid mutiny. Soldiers insist on their right to destroy their own health.

I have heard of an eminent surgeon who has saved countless lives, who carries out five- and six-hour long operations without smoking but chain-smokes as soon as he is out of the theatre. He explains: 'I can do my work *because* I chain-smoke.'

That's how advanced, superior Westerners behave, who often shake their heads with disapproving superiority over Third World foolishness.

When reason meets unreason – as a wise gentleman at WHO remarked – unreason always wins. In the West as well as in the 'Developing Countries'. Perhaps it *is* One World, after all.

Who's Who?

When people heard that I was about to write this book, and that the World Health Organisation was going to help me with my researches, quite a few of them (mostly employees or ex-employees of WHO) volunteered the low-down on the organisation. They told me many simple or involved, reasonable or paranoid stories about WHO, based mostly on their own personal experiences. The gist of all this gossip was that WHO was a bureaucracy and a hotbed of intrigue. I dismissed these tales, not because I did not believe them but because I was aware of these facts before any of my informants opened their mouths. *All* big organisations are bureaucracies and *none* is free of intrigue. I suspected from the first that WHO was no exception, simply because no exceptions exist.

The charge of 'bureaucracy' is, usually, raised on two levels. People imply that so-called 'faceless' bureaucrats are just pampered fillers-in of forms, superfluous para-sites who ride on the necks of creative workers. People utter this condemnation of bureaucrats with the same air of contempt as they apply to politicians (all crooks) and generals (all stupid). But it is not the most intelligent half of humanity which is wont to utter such generalisations. The real aim of such pronouncements is to prove the superiority of the man who makes them. I am far from convinced that all the people who talk like that are really superior to Winston Churchill, or Mrs Thatcher, or even to Neil Kinnock (all politicians). Not every Poly lecturer is superior to Field Marshal Montgomery or Napoleon Bonaparte (soldiers). But coming to bureaucrats: how-ever regrettable this may be, they are necessary. It may be a great pity, but no organisation can function without them. No organisation – be it a newspaper, a factory or a complex international body – can do without people who plan, hire and furnish their buildings, pay in the incom-ing cheques to the bank, pay out salaries and expenses, settle bills, engage and dismiss people, look after pension funds etc.

'But,' some would object, 'this is only too obvious. We do not object to the existence of bureaucrats, only to their excesses.' That's not, in fact, what they usually say but we'll let it pass. And we will admit that complaint about bureaucratic excesses is perfectly justified. The fact that bureaucrats can become over-ambitious, over-whelming and power-hungry shows that they, too, are human (which may come as a surprise to many people). When this happens, rap them on the knuckles, by all means. Accountants should not run the factory; managers of the advertising department should not be allowed to dictate the policy of a newspaper; and permanent under-secretaries should not be permitted to play the part of the minister.

About intrigues. Of course, they must be rampant. I have never yet seen a large organisation – or a small one, for that matter – where brotherly love reigned supreme and where X was more anxious to see Y promoted than himself.

I do not know what the exact situation at WHO is in these matters, and I never even tried to find out. The position, probably, is no better and no worse than in other huge organisations. I am not interested. What I am interested in is this: can such a large international organisation do any good, whoever runs it?

The real difficulties of WHO lie elsewhere. WHO is a multinational organisation but not a supra-national one. It is not very easy to draw the line between the two. The UN itself often tries to be supra-national instead of being a catalyser; or else – vis-à-vis a completely unreasonable and recalcitrant tiny state – they go on catalysing instead of kicking it in the shins with total super-power consent.

WHO must remain strictly non-political. Easier said than done. To refrain from being political in a thoroughly politicised world is about as easy as to refrain from breathing. If a country suffers from floods or droughts that, for its government, is a *political* disaster; if the harvest is good, and brings high prices for the farmers, almost full employment and general prosperity in its wake, that is a triumph for the government. So even the weather is strongly political. How can WHO remain more neutral than the weather?

Governments are always trying to use WHO to their own ends and WHO's very *raison d'être* is *to be used by governments;* which sounds most convenient – until you remember how many kinds of 'using' are possible, whereupon it's quite easy to see that WHO's position is not always easy.

If an African government authorises a general campaign of immunisation and the campaign is a success, then the government is praised. If the campaign – rightly or wrongly – is held responsible for the death of babies, the effect of the despair and anger generated is also strongly political. But the problem, of course, causes difficulties on more sophisticated levels, too.

While it is true that every act of WHO may be – and is – regarded as political, it is also true that many political decisions affect general health. Governments try to reduce inflation. Everybody agrees with that in principle. Who wants inflation? But the reduction of inflation (don't we know it?) creates unemployment and unemployment, in turn, means the worsening of general health and, indeed, often means an increase in the death-rate. Or: in some cases the International Monetary Fund is prepared to pull a country out of the mess in which it landed itself, but on certain conditions only. These conditions, as a rule, affect people's standard of living, and consequently their health, in an adverse way. Or, as a final example, take a government's attitude to cigarette smoking. Cigarette smoking is a killer of taxpayers but also a sustainer of treasuries. Every Chancellor or Finance Minister needs money in order (among other things) to improve people's health. So cigarette smoking is reluctantly and discreetly encouraged. A lot of people must die so that their health may be improved.

The building of hospitals carries great prestige in Developing Countries. And it is a prestigious achievement in the West, too. A new hospital is an impressive sight and reassuring proof that the authorities *care*. Vaccination, on the other hand, carries much less prestige. It is often regarded with suspicion or even hostility in Third World countries. But if we leave the world of emotion and descend to the world of figures, we find a very different relationship between hospital-building and vaccination programmes.

A district has – let us say – one million inhabitants. It gets a new hospital opened by the Prime Minister, and the ceremony, of course, is televised all over the land and reported in all the papers (with pictures). The hospital is modern and well equipped and it has five thousand

31

beds available annually, i.e. five beds per thousand inhabitants, which is inadequate. Nevertheless, it is a tremendous improvement on having no beds at all. The building cost of the hospital is $15m, money having been supplied by WHO as well as by other sources. But the upkeep of the hospital costs a fortune, a daily $200 per bed, which means $1m *a day* and it also means 365 million dollars a year – and all that for one million people. Primary care (which means looking after water supplies, immunisation of children and other preventative measures) costs $15m. And the immunisation of one child costs only three dollars. This last figure means that for the annual cost of one single bed ($200 a day, $73,000 a year) they could immunise almost 25,000 children. And if they do not immunise those children many more hospital beds will be needed.

It is too often the same sad story. The Developing Country opts for building hospitals and children are therefore not immunised. But the country cannot keep up the hospitals – they do not have the money, they do not have enough doctors, they do not have nurses and other skilled staff – so the hospitals deteriorate and have to close.

Yet, governments refuse to learn. Showing the opening of the grand new hospital and broadcasting the Prime Minister's moving speech is wonderful propaganda. To show a few crying babies pricked by a menacingly long needle, watched by a suspicious mother, is positive counter-propaganda. A few weeks or months later you can show again the hospital full of happy and smiling patients (those howling with pain will not be shown) but you cannot possibly *show* all those babies and children who did *not* get whooping cough or dysentery because they got that prick with the nasty needle. A year later the hospital will be crumbling and perhaps be closed. But who cares? Who remembers? No one will mention the subject, nor will anyone speak of those innumerable children who die because they were not immunised.

The world's largest hospital is – or at least was at one time – in Japan (where it was run very efficiently). The ruler of one Middle Eastern state could hardly bear this thought: the largest hospital must be build in his land. It *was*. A hospital bigger than the Japanese. Within two years this giant super-hospital had to be closed and now it is rotting away, a huge empty wreck. But this is not seen as important. What *is* important is this: for a while it was the largest hospital in the world.

Horrible – but preventable – diseases kill millions of people every year. Stupidity and snobbery kill more or, put in another way: stupidity and snobbery are responsible for many of these deaths. But, alas, stupidity and snobbery are not preventable diseases. To eradicate smallpox was comparatively easy. To eradicate stupidity? And snobbery? Who would even try?

Fishing

'Whenever the expression "in the long run" is used,' said one of WHO's pundits, 'the chorus goes up: "In the long run we'll all be dead." Quite. Keynes was right when he made this remark, but by today it has become the cynics' charter and an excuse of not looking ahead.

'In our work the difference between the short run and the long run has a decisive significance. The "long run", is the solution. But the whole thing is not so simple.

'If there is a starving tribe living, let us say, by a river, you may help them in one of two ways. You may give them fish – temporary relief – or else you may teach them how to catch fish, which will solve their problem for good.'

I wanted to raised some objections, but before I could say anything, he raised those objections himself.

'A starving man needs fish and not lessons. True enough. On the other hand when he is not starving, he refuses to learn anything. And here you have one of our basic problems in a nutshell.'

The Dangers of a Healthy Life

'Jogging is the second greatest killer. Worse than the cholera.' This is a statement I have often made, referring, however, to the West where cholera has been eliminated but where the habit of jogging is spreading. (The disease of *marathonitis* has now to be added to *joggitis*.) There was a shade of exaggeration in this but perhaps I have been a little unfortunate in losing more friends through this modern mania than the average citizen. Exercise is supposed to be good for you; but I know that it can be very bad for you. And quite apart from exercise, I have been watching the various health-maniacs with a great deal of suspicion for a long time. But I had to admit that my suspicion was based on instinct, not on knowledge. At last, at WHO, I had an opportunity of discussing these matters with recognised experts. I was glad to find that most of their factual knowledge supported my instincts and prejudices.

35

A man I was chatting to here in London told me the other day: 'I am enjoying bad health.'

'Well, as long as you enjoy it...' I was inclined to say, but did not because it was obvious that he had tried to express himself with a bit of flourish and failed to hit upon the most appropriate phrase. So I told him instead 'You suffer from malnutrition.'

This took him aback.

'I thought my trouble was that I was eating too much.'

I did not elaborate on the subject but that was exactly what I had in mind. *Malnutrition* simply means the wrong way of feeding oneself and it should apply (although it doesn't) to eating too much as well as to eating too little or eating the wrong kind of food.

I was told by one of the WHO experts: 'Modern Western man is too inactive. He just doesn't *do* enough. The human body has been created for a certain amount of physical activity. Normal life means the intake of a certain amount of food which must be balanced with the output of a certain amount of energy. A man's body-weight should be watched and it should remain constant.'

My unhealthy friend, quoted above, was in a sedentary job which he enjoyed immensely, even more than bad health. He was the receptionist at the spare parts department of a huge car-manufacturing firm. Van- and lorry-drivers as well as ordinary private motorists told him what they needed, if they knew it. If not, he told *them* what they needed. Joe knew everything. All the innumerable spare parts, every screw, heft, shaft, shank and gasket, and their catalogue numbers. He was indispensable and he loved it. Who doesn't? But his job was not physically strenuous. He was sitting at his counter all day, writing out little chits for the various departments and taking the money for people's purchases. He was surprised to find that he was growing fatter and fatter although he was not eating more than before and, indeed, had cut down on starch and beer.

'We are so inactive,' continued the WHO expert, 'that we cannot eat little enough. People think that two extra pieces of bread per day is neither here nor there. But two extra pieces of bread may make a great difference. It is difficult to resist temptation. It is all around us. Food manufacturers and supermarkets encourage us to eat more than we need. The food they sell is meant to whet our appetite. Spices and fat induce us to eat more. And remember: one hundred extra and superfluous calories per day means 36,500 calories per year.'

Now we came to my favourite hobby-horse. Some time ago I cut my finger and a caring lady told me to go home and put some disinfectant on the wound. I told her I was quite all right – besides, I had no disinfectant at home. 'Impossible,' she declared in a firm voice. 'Every first-aid kit contains disinfectant.' – 'That's possible,' I nodded, 'but I don't have a first-aid kit. I have some milk of magnesia at home and that's all. I used to have aspirins, too, but I forgot to buy any in the last two or three years. I must make a note of it. One should really have aspirins at home.' The lady refused to believe me. She asked me as a last triumphant argument: 'And what about vitamin tablets? Surely you must take vitamin tablets?'

I have never had a vitamin tablet in the house. In fact, I have no idea what the difference between Vitamins A,B,C,D,E and F is. Neither do I care. Nevertheless, the lady's horrified exclamation and her absolute conviction that no one could possibly survive without vitamin tablets lingered on. Now at last, I had a chance of discussing vitamin tablets with a world-authority.

'Absolutely useless,' the world-authority said firmly. 'All I can say for them is that they are not harmful.'

Well, that's something, I thought. More than one can say about a lot of other famous drugs.

'In fact,' he continued, 'they may do some incidental

good. Many health problems, as we all know, are psychosomatic. While the tablets do no good whatever to the body, in many cases they reassure the mind. Just like horoscopes or magic. That's on the positive side. Yes: these tablets are in the same brackets as horoscopes or magic.'

This was all music to my ears. It is satisfying when an ignorant man like myself proves to be wiser than many highly-regarded authorities.

I then mentioned another pet aversion of mine: health food. When I see a health-food shop, I cross the road. This is perhaps unjust. I am sure they do no definite harm either. They too must be in the horoscope and magic category.

'Health food?' said the gentleman who knew: 'Not much in it. They sell brown bread. Now brown bread is good for you, but *their* brown bread is no better than the one you get at the supermarket or at the baker's on the corner. They also sell brown sugar. They seem to think that everything brown is good for you. But there is no special value in brownness in general or in brown sugar in particular. It is simply sugar that hasn't gone through the last stage of cleaning.'

'Which means,' I remarked, 'that in fact it is not so clean as white sugar.'

'Well, it is clean enough. It's not really *worse* than white sugar. Nor is it any better.'

'Here and there they may score,' he added. 'Unsprayed fruit may be better than sprayed fruit. They used to sell – perhaps they are still selling – unsprayed fruit from Pakistan. If they say that it *is* unsprayed I must believe them. But sometimes that fruit needs spraying. It may be better sprayed. Those chemicals must be most carefully washed off before consumption, that's all.'

I asked him about the yoghurt mania. He shrugged his shoulders. 'All those ancient Bulgars. I don't really know. Never been to Bulgaria. They are supposed to be over a hundred and still rushing around and playing football. And it is all due to yoghurt. It is true, of course, that if you go on eating yoghurt for a hundred and twenty years you become an old man. But I doubt that there is any other connection between yoghurt and old age.'

He thought that the selling of health food was essentially a clever commercial gimmick. After this dismissal of health-shops even I started feeling a little sympathy, so I put in a good word for them: 'They may not be much good. Except in the case of eggs.'

'Why eggs?' he asked.

'Fresh eggs must be better than non-fresh eggs.'

'Not at all. It makes no difference whatsoever whether an egg – as long as it is still all right – is one day or one week old. What does make a difference is: what the chicken was fed on. If it was fed on fish and not maize, I find the egg disgusting. But even those fishy chickens or eggs aren't harmful.'

Having thus buried health food, I returned to jogging.

He repeated all the sensible and well known things about jogging. That it is all right in moderation, and such. Yes, it can be risky for some people, but I was exaggerating wildly when I said that it is killing more people than cholera. For a number of people jogging is becoming a mania, a perversity and an obsession.

'A drug?' I asked. 'Is it more or less dangerous than heroin?'

'Not in the same category. In rare cases, I suppose, it may be more dangerous because it may kill more quickly. People should be on the lookout. Jogging often does become a dangerous obsession.'

I asked him what should a modern, Western executive do? What sort of life should he lead?

'If he is used to a sporting life – including jogging – he should go on. If not, he should do something: walking, swimming, even – provided his heart is all right – climbing stairs will do good. He must lead a more physical life than most of them do.'

He stopped for a moment.

'Another word of caution. And it should be considered by millions who play some ball-game, or swim or skate or ski or whatever. When they reach a certain age – sometimes no more than forty – they give it all up. They say they are too old although they are just too busy or too lazy. But it must be remembered that *exercise has no lasting effect*. It does you no retrospective good. If you stop, you are no better off than someone else who has never done it. So you may as well save yourself the trouble. On the other hand, if you enjoy it and want to derive real benefit, go on and on and on.'

'Until you collapse.'

'I realise that this is a joke,' he said gloomily. 'The point is that one is more likely to collapse if one does nothing than if one leads an active life, in moderation.'

(Which – perhaps quite unjustly – reminded me of Mark Twain's remark: 'Water taken in moderation can do you no harm.')

The Threat of Democracy

What a different picture it is when we look at the Third World.

(Whenever I write down the phrase the *Third World*, I stop and hesitate for a while. Shall I say *Third World* or do I prefer *Developing Countries?* I dislike such euphemisms. I prefer to call a dustman a dustman and not a refuse collecting officer, and a dog a dog, not a house-guarding agent. The dustman is not a collector and not an officer, the dog is no agent. *Dustman* is an honest, precise and time-honoured description of a decent, hard and important job. Besides, it is offensive to call them *refuse collecting officers* as if there was something shameful in their job which ought to be papered over. And a dog is a dog is a dog. I do not like talking of a *liquidity problem* when someone is bankrupt and of a *virility problem* when someone is impotent. Moving into an altogether different sphere, the *cult of personality* was the most revolting

41

euphemism of all – as if we meant the venal sin of excessive vanity and not the mass-murder and torture of millions. But reverting to our present subject: *we*, the West, are in fact (let us hope), the Developing Countries. Though we may, of course be the *Declining World*. Maybe we ought to talk of the Declining World facing the Backward World? But I am an optimist and I believe that we are the Developing World. This phraseology also underlines our obligation to the poorer half. If *they* are developing in any case, why should we bother about them? But having made my views clear on this subject, I am going to return to conventional language. People have always been very sensitive about the truth and I do not mean to be offensive.)

So, as I was saying, there is a very different situation in the Third World. Many Third World countries do need Vitamin A but they cannot get enough of it. Their diet is deficient and lacks, among other things, animal fats. Fat is very expensive. Fats produce Vitamin A (as I have just learnt).

They lack cereals, too. And (perhaps most important of all), they lack iron. Pregnant women are the worst off because the foetus takes away the little iron they get. An iron tablet a day would make a great difference.

But there is a snag here. Good iron tablets are very expensive. They can, however, be produced locally and reasonably cheaply. But these cheap iron tablets cause nausea so women reject them and regard them as harmful or downright evil.

While here in the West we take unnecessary tablets and eat sham health-food the Third World cannot get a proper diet. WHO – and some others – are doing their best but the population of the world grows and the supply of protein is getting shorter and shorter.

Distribution of the available food is a pressing problem as we all know, having read a great deal about Ethiopia and a few other regions. As Dr H (I was asked not to name WHO grandees) explained to me: 'In the Third World, people in the various capitals enjoy many benefits but in the rural areas they suffer. As 85 per cent of the Third World populations live in rural areas this is not a rosy picture. When they get sick, it is always difficult and often impossible to get them into hospital in time or at all. There is no transport; and if they can find transport they do not have roads.'

Dr H believes that by AD 2000 the world will have made satisfactory progress. The year 2000 is not far ahead but for a sick man it seems to be far enough. 'People,' he adds, 'expect a world organisation to lift a magic wand. But there is no magic wand. Yet, the fact that something cannot be done immediately or quickly is no excuse for not doing it at all.'

When Dr H tells me that prevention of disease starts with education, I nod knowledgeably. But political leaders do not nod. By the time half – a quarter, one eighth – of their population is more or less adequately educated, or at least literate, they will not be in power; they will not be alive.

But there are possible short-cuts everywhere. Apart from general education, health specialists are needed everywhere. 'Health specialist' is a nebulous expression. Some people would be inclined to be slightly irritated by it: *health specialists* are doctors, so let's call them doctors. Doctors are, of course, health specialists but in addition to doctors there are the fully trained nurses; in addition to the fully trained nurses there are the partially trained nurses; and in addition to *them* a number of people may be trained in simple (and often not so simple) special jobs. And here is a glimmer of hope for that famous 'in the long run'. Doctors in the Third World countries are not only healers but also teachers. And it is fortunate that utterly uneducated, even totally illiterate – but otherwise naturally intelligent – people may be taught to perform very difficult and complicated special jobs. The

43

nurses, half-trained nurses and specialist illiterates are as important for a country's general health as hospitals.

But here, once again, political complications raise their ugly heads. WHO, trying to achieve this genuine improvement 'in the long run' is often faced with a dreadful charge: it tries to smuggle in democracy through the back door. Health-education, the training of more and more nurses and specialists – so the charge runs – means increased participation, and participation, in turn, leads to democracy. And that's something most of the rulers abhor.

Democracy, of course, is far from being a perfect political system. Accordingly to Churchill's famous dictum, the one thing that can be said in its favour is that all the other systems are worse. Be that as it may, it must be acknowledged that many African and other Third World countries are not ripe for a Westminster-type of democracy. That is true. But a simplified version would do. This, however, is no argument in the eyes of rulers who are suspicious of any dose and any form of democracy. But perhaps WHO and others may persuade them that teaching a few hundred or a few thousand illiterate tribesmen how to give injections and first aid, and how to dress wounds, does not threaten the grip of tyrants. Indeed, it might make people more contented, and consequently more docile and subservient. As this type of education may thus produce *more tyranny through the back-door*, the outlook is not hopeless.

The Heart of the Monkey

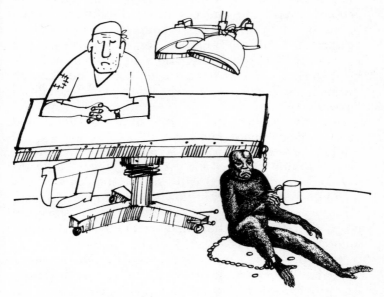

For a while every conversation I had at the Headquarters of WHO convinced me that humanity lives on two different planes and that problems of the First World have nothing to do with the problems of the Third.

Then, the more I heard and the more I listened, I saw that this assumption was wrong. We are all the same animal, we all belong to the same species, although many people refuse to accept that. Yes, dividing lines are important; differences seem painful and often look unbridgeable. Yet, all these differences are superficial.

Just to mention (and in one or two cases repeat) some essential facts. The Third World suffers from different diseases, many of them eradicated in the West. About 60 per cent of their diseases are caused by contaminated water, while our water is clean. (Many Friends of the Earth and other environmentalists hotly deny this, but the truth is that tap water in Europe is not less healthy than mineral water which an increasing number of people drink – quite unnecessarily.) If we are ill we can be taken to hospital. What happens to us in some hospitals is a different question, but the roads exist and we can get there quickly. We do maintain our hospitals in reasonable order even if many of them do not have all the facilities they desire and even if some are closed down for economic reasons.

But 'civilisation', to use this imprecise shorthand word, is no solution. The sad truth is that nothing is a solution. *There is no solution to any problem.* Inevitably, every solution creates new problems. These problems may be minor compared with the previous ones (that's how humanity progresses, slowly and painfully), nevertheless, problems they are. They have to be solved in order that their solution may create new and other unforeseen problems.

What problems can civilisation create? Numerous.

We have invented the motor car and love it. It creates vast problems. It pollutes the air of great cities as well as of small villages. It causes many accidents. African tribal villagers with no roads in the district, are not knocked down by fast sports cars. Our children are. Another blessing inflicted on us by our beloved motor car is that we walk about less and less and as a result, suffer from more and more ill-health.

Other mechanical inventions cause similar problems. The Finnish lumberjacks of Karelia used to be among the healthiest specimens of humanity. They hardly knew what heart-disease was. The last one or two generations changed all this. Today the incidence of heart trouble among them is high, in fact, among the highest in the world. Why? Because not too long ago they started using electric saws and exerted much less effort than before, led more comfortable lives and as a result of this they also changed their eating habits. These sturdy Finns of

Karelia now do what so many others do in the City of London, or in Duesseldorf and Amsterdam boardrooms: they move less and eat more.

It is true that civilisation freed us – the West – of a number of diseases, but we poison ourselves, and our descendants, with the products of civilisation. We inhale industrial chemicals, smoke, the exhaust fumes of engines etc.

Civilisation also creates new forms of crime. Every new invention brings a new wave of crime in its wake. When the unbreakable safe was invented, the underworld regarded it – so to say – as a matter of honour to break it. And they did. When the Welfare State is set up people cheat millions out of it by false claims. Now computer crimes are becoming more and more fashionable. In the villages of Africa or Central America computer-hackers are extremely rare.

Civilisation means more suicides and more alcoholism. Drug addiction is somewhat different: it is widespread even among backward tribes, too. Civilisation means more cancer. Whether this is due to more smoking or to other reasons is debatable.

One further remark on drug addiction. Hundreds of thousands of South American peasants prefer to grow coca to growing wheat. Coca, the killer, the father of cocaine, brings in ten times as much money as wheat. So they grow coca. In this they behave like civilised people in the West.

I said earlier that jogging was the second largest killer in the West. The first (in the West), to my utterly unscientific mind, is hygienics. Overcleaning, keeping away all (well, as many as possible) bacilli, bacteria and viruses undermines our power of resistance. So-called uncivilised villagers can happily eat food which would kill many over-hygienic Americans and Europeans.

As soon as backward villagers are taught to live a more hygienic life, they start falling victim to diseases which formerly did them no harm.

Hygeia used to be the Greek Goddess of Good Health. She had nothing to do with diseases or cures. Man would remain healthy with her help if he led a reasonable life. Hygeia could be the Goddess of WHO. She is all Prevention – the ultimate ideal.

Civilisation, the Reader may object, is no Paradise, we all know that. But where is the similarity between the European town dweller, driver of fast cars and supporter of opera houses, and the primitive tribesman who has no access to uncontaminated water?

I heard the answer many times and in many forms at WHO. The general line of thought is this. It is an accepted axiom (I must say it again) that prevention is preferable to treatment. If someone, say, breaks his leg, treatment must be *retroactive* and so it must be in all cases when someone has already caught a disease. Prevention, avoidance of disease, is better; and education – teaching people how to avoid danger, how not to break their limbs and how to kill bacteria before bacteria kill them – is better still. Yet, this is not the whole story. Health – people at WHO keep repeating it with impressive sincerity – is something more than the mere absence of disease. Health should mean complete physical and mental well-being. 'Ultimately,' Dr H told me, 'it is people who make themselves sick.' You may call it worrying, or stress or strain. The elimination of pressure is as important as the elimination of bacteria. And this is where the difference between the Developed and the Undeveloped World disappears. One man worries about a snake-bite, the other about losing his job or about the fall of share-prices, but worry remains worry, the effect is the same. Religion is as much the source of strain as economic matters. One may worry about having committed a mortal sin and the other may feel persecuted by the Evil Spirit of the Forest – the result on their health will not differ. Western man eats, drinks and often works

48

too much; Third World man also works too much but does not eat enough. In that they differ. But both of them live under stress and in fear. They are brothers.

Western man relies on technical and mechanical solutions in everything. Refrigerators preserve his food, washing machines clean his underwear and computers are supposed to solve all his problems. When ill, he relies on the surgeon's scalpel. If the old heart is running down it must be repaired; if it cannot be repaired it should be replaced, just as an old car sometimes gets a new engine. But up to now we have had a shortage of hearts: to keep one man alive another man had to die. There is more and more talk in certain circles about the jungle. About monkeys. Every monkey has a near-human heart and humanity has never been over-scrupulous in respecting the lives and well-being of animals (including the lives and well-being of the human animal). Therefore in the year 2000 or thereabouts – I was told – a massacre of monkeys may occur. We'll cut out their hearts for human consumption.

Monkeys, on the whole, are happier creatures than their near relatives, Homo Sapiens. They know fear, of course, and they face real dangers, but they are more intelligent than us. They create no imaginary and unnecessary dangers for themselves; they run no businesses; chase no money; are unimpressed by gold – that utterly useless metal; and they do not give a damn about hell or the evil eye. I have a vague feeling that it is not monkeys' hearts we ought to implant in us, but monkeys' brains.

Time, the Eternal Problem

I visited many departments at WHO, talked to many heads of departments and other experts and asked a lot of questions. The questions tried to elucidate problems which interested me, a layman. In the following few chapters I shall give the gist of the answers received in the hope that the answers will interest other laymen too.

I have often heard that the West is an easy winner (if that be the right expression) in one of the worst killing diseases: heart trouble, or more scientifically: cardio-vascular diseases.

Dr D confirmed this. The reasons for this state of affairs are pretty obvious. Heart diseases are what doctors call multi-factoral ailments. Three of the important factors are: (1) too much fat – coupled with being overweight; (2) smoking and (3) lack of exercise.

I have already spoken about the problem of lack of exercise, so I shall add very little here to the subject. Dr D made a point not mentioned by others. He said that habitual exercise creates a general feeling of well-being. More precisely: in addition to the actual beneficial results, the knowledge that you are an active man, leading a healthy life, adds to your well-being. The euphoria thus created may be partly physical (simply: exercise is good for you) and partly mental: you feel virtuous and healthy – perhaps in some cases, healthier than you really are. A permanent psychological pat on your own shoulders cheers you up. Dr D added, however, that even habitual and reasonable exercise will not necessarily prevent heart disease, except indirectly: it reduces weight.

Humanity tends to commit suicide. It keeps making pretty good attempts at it. Wars – international and civil – as well as 'purges', concentration camps, mass persecutions, acts of terror in support of a few good and many crazy causes (not that a good cause justifies terrorism) – all these are intended to liquidate 'the enemy'. As the victims are human beings killed by other human beings it all amounts to a sui-genocidal attempt. One of the most effective weapons of sui-genocide is smoking – which is killing more people than terrorists. Drugs help too. Smoking and drug-taking are widespread all over the world but they are most widespread in the West.

Yet, no dogma is universally true. Alcohol is also one of the known poisons, so some noble creatures preach total abstinence. But these preachers, while extremely high-minded, are not quite so wise as they think. It is an established fact that people who consume alcohol in moderation live longer than teetotallers. But I must add: they also live longer than heavy drinkers. Heavy drinking produces more cholesterol, high blood-pressure and cardio-myopathy. In other words: heavy drinking attacks the heart and also ruins the liver. Many heavy drinkers depend on a simple way out: they succeed in persuading themselves that they are, in fact, moderate drinkers. A good line, but not always effective.

51

Oversalting of food is also a Western mania. (A mania which I share. I am one of those barbarians who first salt a dish and then taste it.) Oversalting – says Dr D and many others – is bad for you. No one can live without salt (sodium), the body needs it. But too much salt may cause a lot of complications. Five grams a day is regarded as the optimum, ten or fifteen grams are dangerous. But there is no absolute rule here. How much salt is really dangerous depends on habits – you may get used to many things – and genetic disposition.

I asked Dr D about cholesterol. Medical gentlemen, in one respect, are like philosophers. When a philosopher declares something – whatever this may be – three others will rush in to state the opposite. Medical scientists act in the same way. From time to time even the most widely accepted, almost sacred, doctrines are challenged. Certain ingredients hitherto regarded as poison are declared to be essential requirements of good health. One such villain is cholesterol. Like everybody else I have heard that cholesterol, consumed mostly in the form of animal fats, is a deadly poison. I have disregarded this. I do not plan to live forever and I think that poisoning oneself with sausages, bacon, pork chops etc. is a reasonably pleasant way of dying. As far as I know (and I may be wrong, of course) all this cholesterol has done me no harm, and has not made that pleasant death imminent. We shall see. (Well, if I am wrong, I shall not see.) Then – when I was resigned to the poisonous effects of cholesterol – a new theory emerged. Cholesterol is necessary, cholesterol is good for you and, indeed, lack of cholesterol may cause cancer.

I asked Dr D about this. It is not in dispute, he explained, that cholesterol is important. The brain needs cholesterol to do its work. Cholesterol is prepared from animal and vegetable fats, either low-density or high-density lipo-proteins or lipids. The high-density protects, the low-density is more harmful because it infiltrates more easily. The main danger of cholesterol is that it narrows or blocks the arteries. All arteries may be affected. The accepted theory is – or was – that animal fats are the more dangerous and egg-yolks are also rich in it.

But what about the new and far from generally accepted theory that cholesterol is all right, in fact, useful? Dr D said that while investigations are still proceeding he refused to believe that too little cholesterol might be dangerous. Although he expressed himself in polite and moderate terms I have the impression that he thought this theory was utter rubbish. 'Low cholesterol,' he declared, 'does not seem to be a medical problem.'

So the general doctrine is that obesity, overweight, lack of exercise, genetic disposition, too much salt and too much cholesterol may cause heart-troubles. We also know that stress and strain are important factors in causing heart-diseases. Contrary views were expressed in the last chapter. Dr D thinks that Western men live under greater stress than people of the Third World. To drive along in fast cars on motorways (as a way of life) is more stressful than to be pulled along by two buffaloes on a mud-track – even if you are accompanied by four wives. (I am not quite sure about the stressfulness of having four wives: perhaps one wife can alleviate the stress caused by another, two can alleviate the stress caused by the other two? I would not really know. I never had four wives – not at one and the same time.)

There is a similar dispute concerning salt. The Medical Research Council's Blood-Pressure Unit at Glasgow, and medical schools in Leicester, New York, Sweden and New Zealand have declared that while some individuals might be helped by salt reduction others might be harmed. They maintain that to suggest a universal reduction in salt-intake is 'unjustified and irresponsible'.

They do not accept the evidence that reduction in salt-intake reduces blood-pressure. A doctor wrote a letter to the *Lancet* and remarked that no work had been done to show that patients on salt-reduced diets are at less risk of strokes or heart-attacks than others. The medical researchers quoted above go even further: they allege that salt-reduction, in fact, may have harmful effects. They have experimented with rats. Salt-reduced diet has caused stunted development and, in some cases, *increased* blood-pressure. Even if salt-reduction is beneficial for some people with high blood-pressure, (and this is far from proved, they add), to recommend a salt-free or salt-reduced diet to the population as a whole is quite wrong because the great majority of people have normal blood-pressure and only a small minority suffers from hypertension. The MRC unit adds that they are not even convinced that the present intake of salt in Western countries causes high blood-pressure. Differences in the prevalence of hypertension in different societies are impressive but may be due to a wide range of dietary and other factors.

Well, if our most eminent medical societies – people who spend their lives dealing with these problems – disagree, what is the poor layman to do? Cut out cholesterol? Increase it? Reduce salt intake? Or oversalt his food? It is difficult to be a dietary expert but it is much more difficult to be an ordinary layman who tries to live a healthy life.

There is one factor which does more harm to Western man than salt and cholesterol put together. It is consistent hurry; being always pressed for time.

There are two pseudo-virtues we, in the West, tend to respect: modesty and punctuality. They are both somewhat repulsive virtues, nearer to vices than to true virtues. (May I make it clear that I am not trying to pat myself on the back and dress up my own failings as virtues. I am a reasonably modest man – one who believes that he has a great deal to be modest about – and I have tried, throughout a lifetime, to cure myself of the habit of obsessive punctuality. So I am not castigating others; I am castigating myself.)

The question of modesty does not concern us here. Punctuality does. We are inclined to speak with disapproval, often with contempt, of those happy Latins, Italians, Spaniards and even more Brazilians – who make an appointment for three o'clock on Wednesday afternoon and then may stroll in at any time after five, or on Thursday morning, or not at all. I have a sneaking admiration for their nonchalant attitude. I know, of course, that modern society cannot be organised without adherence to a strict timetable. I also admit that I am not particularly pleased if a dinner guest arrives three-quarters of an hour late or when I am kept waiting twenty minutes although I have turned up punctually for an appointment. In such cases I am more likely than not to walk out, however important the appointment may be for me. Having said all that, I instinctively admire the Latins' cavalier treatment of time. I prefer it to being a slave to the clock. Slavery is not only a moral bondage, it is also a deadly enemy of good health. Permanent rushing from one place to another, constant worrying about being late is an incessant pressure on Western man completely unknown to Masai tribesmen.

(Talking of the Masai, there is a riddle there. Stress and constant hurrying raises blood pressure. Anger raises it even more. It has been found, however, after thorough studies and experiments, that even the most violent anger does not raise the blood-pressure of the Masai. No one can explain this.)

I am, as I have said before, a maniacally punctual man. But this mania causes no strain in me. I do not rush. I simply start on time.

We all know about the danger of stress, strain and hurry. There is another danger which is not so widely recognised.

A doctor friend asked me what my blood-pressure was. I told her that I had no idea. When did I have my last check-up? – she asked. I had never had one, I told her. (This happened about twenty years ago.) Never in my life? No, never in my life. Did I think this was wise? Yes, I thought it was very wise. If I did not think it wise, I would be rushing to have check-ups all the time. Would I please tell her how I came to this conclusion.

With pleasure. I believe – nay, I *know*, I am sure – that if you have any sort of trouble, disorder, difficulty, irregularity or illness, it will manifest itself in one way or another. You will learn about it. You may feel pain; you may feel dizzy; or tired; you may lose your appetite; you may have difficulties in breathing. Nature has innumerable ways of conveying the message. If you notice any symptom, go and see your doctor. But constant check-ups just create a neurosis: your blood-pressure will go up, the state of your health will deteriorate. Innocent symptoms will indicate cancer; if you catch a cold in the middle of February you will diagnose chronic bronchitis. Do I take in enough alcohol? Do I take in too much cholesterol? Or not enough? Too many eggs? Too much salt? These check-ups may turn you into a hypochondriac. Or you must have been a hypochondriac to need all those check-ups. All this worrying about your health may do more harm to your health than all the bacilli, cholesterol and salt put together.

This, however, is an attitude hard to learn, even if someone wishes to learn it. First of all, a large number of people genuinely need check-ups and they are wise to have them. Second, you cannot persuade a worrying and brooding type of man to be casual and happy-go-lucky any more than you can persuade a short man to be tall or a dark-eyed man to be blue-eyed. (On the other hand you can persuade a dark-haired person to become blonde and a fat person to become thin – so nothing is quite hopeless.)

Dr D did not agree with me. One should regularly check one's blood-pressure but – he agreed – one should refrain from casual check-ups. I still think there is no general rule. Some people must keep an eye on their blood-pressure but others have constant low blood-pressure and they need not worry on that count. They may have to worry for other reasons and they should have the check-ups their doctors advise. But people with no complaints who feel and are healthy, should go and see their doctors only when they have a complaint. In that I differ from Dr D. If I were you I would listen to him; but as I am myself I am listening to myself.

Quite a few years ago I meant to take out a life insurance. Before being accepted, I had to go and see the company's physician. This was, in fact, the first and, up to date, the last, medical check-up in my life. He listened to my heart, took various samples and, in the course of his examination, took my blood-pressure. I had never had my blood-pressure taken before. When he put that rubber band around my arm, I suddenly got alarmed. I thought it might be painful. I was also afraid that my blood-pressure (which, as I have just said, had never been taken before) was exorbitantly high. My heart beat fast and my brow sweated. The doctor took my blood-pressure and said nothing. 'Is it all right?' I asked but he failed to answer and went on with other tests. At the end of it all he told me that he wanted to take my blood-pressure again. This time I knew that it was not such a terrifying and painful experience. I was relaxed and let him go ahead. In the end he said 'I thought so. Your blood-pressure is absolutely normal. First it was almost double of what it should be. Some people [he was too polite to say: 'some fools'] are terrified of their blood-pressure being taken and it all goes awry.'

Perhaps this is the true justification of my attitude. If the fear of my blood-pressure being taken doubles it, then I'd better not have my blood-pressure taken. Too many check-ups would surely send me to an early grave.

Finally, I have just gone through one of the WHO publications (Prevention of Coronary Heart Disease, Geneva, 1982) and I find that although, of course, it uses more scientific language, it agrees with my other informants, except that the book sees cholesterol as a positive danger. About salt-intake it is more doubtful. It lists, however, another potential threat which I did not mention before.

The booklet says that oral contraceptives create a definite (but statistically low) degree of danger. It is only two or three per cent but, needless to say, if you happen to be one of the victims, this percentage is high enough. The danger becomes higher for women over thirty who also smoke and/or have elevated blood-pressure or blood cholesterol and for *all* women above the age of forty.

Drinkers of Infinity

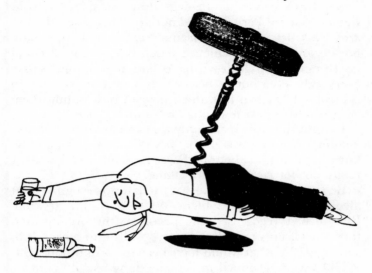

I am no teetotaller but could easily become one, simply not noticing that I did not have a drop of alcohol for weeks, months or years. When it is hot, I quite like a glass of beer; in good company I do enjoy a little wine or a drop of brandy. But I would not miss beer, wine or brandy if I did not see a drop for the rest of my life. I described in another book how Arthur Koestler, a close friend for thirty years, dropped me for a year or so because – as he put it – 'he's a drink bore, he does not drink enough'.

When I was six years old, a man in our village in Hungary took me and a friend of mine of the same age to his vineyard and made us taste wine. We got drunk, both of us. This was supposed to be a superb joke but my father failed to appreciate it. He, a quiet and civilised man, nearly beat up the perpetrator of this joke. This was not only the first but also the very last occasion when I got drunk. One reason for never drinking too much was that I hated the idea of not being in full control of myself. Being drunk seemed to me degrading; surrendering your Ego to your Id. Perhaps I did not drink because I did not *need* drink: I have always been a reasonably happy man, not because I have achieved much but because I could be content with little. I have had my problems like everybody else but – because I meant to remain in control – I tried to face them instead of avoiding them with the help of a few gins and tonics.

I admit that this is not only a so-called virtue but also a failing. Koestler was probably right. I *am* a drink bore, but what can I do about it? Force myself to drink when I really do not care about drinking?

Be that as it may, I was a little late to recognise that alcohol was a major problem. WHO was a bit late, too. But once it recognised the problem, the organisation threw itself energetically into . . . well, into what? Into solving it? No, that would have been over-ambitious. But WHO was determined to do something useful about it.

People like joking about 'yet another committee' or 'yet another study group'. The joking and despair are often fully justified. Committees and study groups are often the final refuges of helpless bureaucrats; 'studying a problem' is often just a synonym for not doing anything about it. On the other hand, you must study a problem before trying to solve it. Only a fool would try to remedy an ill before understanding it.

The first results of the WHO studies were two discoveries:

(1) There seem to be genetic reasons for drinking. The *need* has genetic reasons, and so has the effect of alcohol. Asians, for example, get drunk much more easily than West Europeans or Americans. Why? There is no satisfactory answer to this question. Even within countries – among people of the same genetic origin – there are vast differences. Alcohol consumption and drunkenness may be high in a country where only a small minority – 15 per cent or so – drink at all, but that minority drinks a lot. In

such a country alcoholism may be a graver problem than in another one where nearly everybody drinks, more or less moderately. Drinking habits vary in the same country according to regions and within the same class.

(2) WHO discovered that alcoholism, or heavy drinking, was thought everywhere to be a minority problem, even in countries where everybody was obviously unsteady on his feet after six p.m. The reason for this is that people are inclined to believe that drinking is the other fellow's problem. *They* can carry their drink; *they* can overstep the limit now and then (i.e. every day) with impunity. Other fellows most certainly should refrain from driving a car when drunk; but *they* can take care of themselves and others.

The study groups soon discovered that alcohol poisons the *whole* man and alcohol-related problems poison a whole society. As Dr G remarked: 'Perhaps only the fingernails are immune to heavy drinking. And even that is not quite sure. Drinking affects every organ and function, first of all the liver, then the brain. But it also affects the heart and the kidneys. It affects the nervous system, it causes hallucinations and sexual problems – it causes impotence or near-impotence.'

The deterioration of the human individual affects the entire society. Alcoholics and heavy drinkers become bad at their jobs. As they become impatient, irritable and tense all their human relations deteriorate – within the family and outside it. Heavy drinkers and alcoholics often become violent.

On the day of writing this I have seen two news items in the papers. One expert, who had studied the issue for a long time, declared that the one major issue in football-hooliganism was too much drink. The other item informed us that the President of Singapore had had to resign because he could not control his alcoholism. And who has failed to hear, over and over again, that most car accidents are caused by drunken drivers?

The trend of drinking varies from country to country

61

and from time to time. In North America the habit has become stabilised. In France they drink less than in many other countries but more people suffer from liver-troubles than anywhere else in the world. Drinking is on the increase in Africa and South America. This is most noticeable in Venezuela where sudden riches made alcohol accessible to many who could not afford it before. This information is somewhat strange because one does not need to be rich or well off to drink regularly. Indeed, the most rapid increase in alcohol-intake is the growth of beer consumption in Africa. But as even this is too expensive for many, the consumption of home-distilled drinks is also growing.

Some of the blame lies with the drink-merchants. They are losing some ground in the West so they are trying to acquire new customers in the Developing Countries. 'Acquiring' customers is a euphemism for poisoning them. In the sixteenth and seventeenth centuries the West exterminated whole populations by addicting them to alcohol. So why not try it again? – some people seem to think. All the same, the whole blame must not be put on the shoulders of the drink-merchants. As someone re-marked at WHO: many of them are trying hard· to produce harmless drinks; many of them try to sell soft drinks. But – many of them plead – they have to live. This plea – that they have to live – implies that many of their customers must die.

What is the solution? Even I, usually an incurable optimist, believe that there is no solution. Prohibition in the United States made it plain that banning alcohol is not the answer. Prohibition created gangsterism in America on an unprecedented scale without even decreasing alcohol consumption. Similarly, banning heroin, cocaine and the rest does not solve the drug-problem. Besides, treasuries – like drink-merchants - have to live or – put it in other words – need the revenue. Governments deliver sermons about the evil of alcoholism and heavy drinking and they pocket the revenue. They cry all the way to the bank.

Fathers – often heavy drinkers themselves – wink benevolently when they permit their children the first glass of wine or whisky. That is: to drink it openly in the family circle. But, as likely as not, the kids have tried these pleasures long before. All the same: fathers are proud of their children. Drinking with the adults is a great step towards manhood. In the old days, the first drink was 'officially' permitted when the adolescent became a man; today it is permitted when the child is becoming an adolescent. Who says there is no progress in the world?

This is a superficial explanation. Behind it all lie deeper reasons. I have already mentioned the motive: the general unhappiness of the human race. The *unconscious aim* is self-destruction. Humanity wants to do itself in. Genocide is a word which was coined after the Nazi war. Geno-suicide or sui-genocide is a more relevant notion in our days. Alcohol is more destructive than the nuclear bomb. The bomb is a potential mass-murderer; alcohol is an actual one. The victims of Hiroshima and Nagasaki were killed (mostly) in a short period of time; their number runs to hundred of thousands. A triviality compared with the numbers killed by alcohol through the ages.

WHO does its best. It advocates public health measures; it develops techniques for the 'identification, prevention and management' of alcohol-related problems. It co-operates with governments in the solution of national alcohol problems. It is busy studying the problem and holds frequent conferences. Sometimes I wonder: how many bottles of excellent wine are consumed during these conferences, trying to rid us of the evil of drinking? But this is just a cynical, passing thought. I am sure that giving up these conferences would not be the solution either.

Mental Illness in Two Worlds

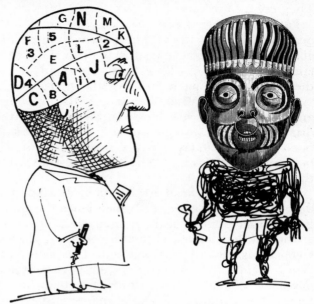

The treatment of mental illness – Dr O of WHO's Mental Health Division told me – has changed direction. 'We used to treat the sick,' he said, 'now we look at all aspects of mental health.'

This does not just mean the usual, and very sensible, idea of prevention being preferred to treatment. General well-being is the key to mental health and that is what WHO's noble utopia means to achieve. But is it possible?

The three main fields of primary concern are: (1) psycho-social factors; (2) mental and neurological disorders; (3) problems created by alcohol and drug-abuse.

Dr O feels – like all caring heads of all departments – that psychology is being neglected. Twenty years ago about half of all hospital beds in the UK were occupied by *long-staying* psychiatric patients. This situation has been remedied. There are fewer people in hospital but there are no fewer sufferers.

Is there a difference in the mental illness field between the West and the Developing World?

Violent people have to be locked up everywhere for their own good but first of all for the good of others. The difference between the two worlds arises when we come to such illnesses as schizophrenia or depression.

There is no need to dwell here on the changed attitude towards the mentally sick. As late as in the last century mad people were thrown into prison, were often kept in chains and were held responsible for their misfortune. The devil got into them and that, obviously, was their own fault. This was the attitude of quite a few Western countries, too.

This has changed by now and we are ready to regard mentally sick people as we regard other sick people. But snobbery intrudes – as it almost always does – and is determined to draw a line between U- and non-U illnesses.

It was about a century ago that Freud and his disciples placed psychology in the forefront of general interest. Various, slighter sort of disorders were given the collective, umbrella-name of *neurasthenia*. To be violent, to be raving mad, was a regrettable but common disease of the vulgar plebs. Very non-U. But *neurasthenia,* as its elegant, classical name suggested, was reserved for the refined, the educated and the well-off. How could an ignorant peasant suffer from *neurasthenia* when he never learnt Greek?

Has this attitude changed in the last few decades? Not entirely.

It was WHO itself who published a monograph by J.C. Caruthers, a British psychiatrist in Kenya. Caruthers restated (in 1953) the old belief of colonial doctors that Africans could not get depressed because of 'the inferior development of their brain'. The opposite of the African – who could not become depressed either – was the Noble Savage. Well, he *could* become depressed but would not because he was a man free of the strains and stresses of urban life. That saved him from the dangers of being depressed, according to Dr Caruthers. All this, however, proved to be utter rubbish. Depressive illnesses – *neurasthenia*, if you like – are as common in Developing Countries as they are in the West and they respond to the same pharmacological treatment as anywhere else.

That is, if people in Developing Countries do get the treatment. The truth is that they rarely get it. Violent people are locked up – violence is very easy to diagnose; but almost everywhere in the Thirld World people suffering from depressions, phobias, neurasthenia, nervous breakdown etc. do not get near a hospital. That makes the job of statisticians rather difficult. It is impossible to make a statistical assessment of the incidence of neurasthenia in the Third World. But the illness is widespread even if we cannot get exact data about it.

Yet, snobbery apart, there seems to be a certain difference between mental illnesses in the Developed Countries and the Third World. Take schizophrenia, for instance. In the West about 35-40 per cent of attacks are malignant and patients never get better. The rest enjoy long periods of improvement but are subject to relapse. In the Developing World about one quarter of the population is subject to a single attack, after which they get better and never relapse.

Borderline cases make statistical comparisons even more difficult. Where is the borderline of true madness? Take one example. Is a person who believes that he is possessed by spirits mad or not? The answer is simple, at least in theory: if he can function properly in society there is no reason to regard him as mad; if he cannot function, he obviously is regarded as mentally sick. In practice the differentiation is not quite so simple.

There are differences in the incidence, severity, attitudes to, and treatment of mental disturbance in different societies and even in different layers of the same society. But these differences are not based on racial grounds. Western man must give up the snobbish pride

66

that he is more depressed and more neurotic than his brother in Developing Countries. They are just as mad as we are. In some respects, we are not as sane as they.

Having spoken of statistics, I cannot resist adding a footnote to this chapter. The footnote does not aspire to be more than a joke. But it is one of those revealing jokes which throw a good deal of light upon a subject. It also complements the old adage, according to which there are lies, bloody lies and statistics. The adage is, of course, a malicious lie itself – it is hard to imagine modern social sciences without statistics. But statisticians have their difficulties. In the absence of data – as we have seen – they are helpless. They cannot tell us how many mentally ill patients in the Thirld World are never even suspected of being mentally ill.

Well, here is the footnote.

In the 1970s a number of planes were blown up by terrorists in mid-air and a worried American business-man went to see a statistician in New York and asked him what the probability was of travelling in a plane which also carried a bomb. The statistician made long calculations and replied: 'One to 16,000.'

'But that's terrifying,' said the businessman. 'Absolutely awful. But, alas, I must travel and there is absolutely nothing I can do about it.'

'Oh yes,' said the statistician, 'there is a lot you can do about it. You can carry your own bomb.'

The businessman thought the statistician had gone out of his mind. Or was suffering, at least, from neurasthenia.

'What the hell do you mean?'

'I should have thought it was obvious. The chances that there is a bomb in a plane are one in 16,000, which is pretty alarming. But the chances that there are *two* bombs in the same plane are one to 27 million – barely worth thinking about. So the answer is in your own hands.'

Travellers

Having ventured to tell that joke I should like to repeat an anecdote which I told in *How to be God*. My excuses are A) that it is particularly revealing about the doctor-patient relationship, B) I heard it from Dr C at WHO, which makes it specially appropriate to these pages, and C) it is most unlikely – reluctant though I am to admit it – that everybody has read all my books.

It concerns as Israeli lady who lives in Tel-Aviv. She visits a specialist in Jerusalem and tells him : 'I have seen two doctors in Tel-Aviv, and they both say that I need an operation. Will you pleased examine me and tell me what you think.'

'A second opinion?'

'A third one.'

The specialist examined her most thoroughly and then gave her his verdict: 'Yes, I fully agree with my colleagues in Tel-Aviv. You do need an operation.'

'Thank-you,' said the lady; and then, after a pause: 'But I shan't have it.'

'May I ask why not?'

'Because I am afraid. I have always been terrified of the idea of putting my life in the hands of a surgeon – it's as simple as that.'

The specialist reflected for a moment, and then said: 'I see. But tell me: how did you travel from Tel-Aviv to Jerusalem?'

'By bus.'

'Who drove the bus?'

'A young man of about twenty-two. Very good-looking, he was, with long hair.'

'So you are prepared to put your life in the hands of a very good-looking long-haired bus-driver of twenty-two, but not into the hands of one of the best and most experienced surgeons in the country?'

The lady nodded. 'There is a tremendous difference, you see. *He* was travelling in the same bus.'

The Pill for Men

WHO's Department for Special Programmes, which is run by Dr B, is a typical product of international bureaucracy – and works very well, not in spite of, but probably because of, this fact. I shall come to its current main project presently, but first I should like to say a little about its organisation.

This Department, as its name indicates, has no single and unchanging purpose but takes on *ad hoc* tasks which may seem important today and be forgotten – or else solved – tomorrow. That is the idea, the principle, behind it. Consequently, Special Programmes, known as SP, has no regular budget allocated to it. I doubt whether any department of anything ever feels that it is given enough money, but SP suffers, in addition to this normal dearth, from not knowing in advance how serious the dearth is going to be. Its leaders must fight and beg

70

from year to year, struggling to convince the nine people on the Board, and about a dozen government agencies representing Developed Countries, and three other agencies, that its new programme deserves generous funding, or – if the project is not new – that it has made enough progress in the past year to deserve full support in the coming one.

The system, Dr B told me, is not wholly a Bad Thing. SP can never rest on its laurels, as some other departments can and do. If it is unable to show progress the money will go elsewhere (there are plenty of claimants waiting in the queue), or will be heavily cut. So SP can never afford to be lazy, which is a healthy state of affairs. But at the same time this stimulating system is also a great nuisance. Many of SP's special programmes are huge and adventurous enterprises: the solution to one single problem may take decades to achieve; and a budget which may be cut – or, indeed, killed – from one year to another makes such a job immensely difficult. It would even be possible, in principle, for SP to pursue a project for fifteen years, and then have to abandon it just as the solution came in sight because the money had dried up. Luckily, however, this doesn't seem to happen in practice. One way or another, Dr B manages to keep his projects going, sometimes with more success, sometimes with less, but always achieving good enough results to push on with his favourite and most important projects.

SP does no field work and provides no services. Its business is research. At present its main preoccupation is human reproduction. One of the problems in this field is lack of fertility – a grave matter for many individuals. But a far more serious problem, affecting the peace – and indeed the entire future – of mankind, is over-population. Infertility concerns about 20 per cent of the world's population; over-population concerns – or ought to concern – all of us.

71

SP's main and most important job at present is trying to regulate fertility and to find new and reliable methods of contraception.

They are, for example – and this is one of the latest of their grand projects – experimenting with pills for men. The Chinese have, in fact, found one: it is a substance extracted from seeds and is called *gossypol*. This Chinese pill does work but, like many drugs, it has disagreeable side-effects. Many men are made sterile for life after taking it, others are sterilised temporarily. And many animals have died as a result of WHO experiments with gossypol. As side-effects go, it seems to me that temporary sterilisation is acceptable (it is, after all, the object of the whole exercise), permanent sterilisation is a bit much, and death is simply not on. This must have been in the mind of one of the gentlemen with whom I discussed gossypol, when he remarked: 'The pill is not as yet perfect.'

But nothing in science, or indeed in life, is straightforward. One might suppose that if gossypol killed animals, then it must also have killed Chinese men. But it has not done so; it has not even made Chinese men sick. True, some of them suffered from temporary paralysis, but they all recovered from that pretty quickly. The relative immunity of Chinese men to this drug may, however, be grounded on one of those inexplicable (or at least hitherto unexplained) differences between one kind of human being and another, so even without the temporary paralysis of some Chinese men, caution must be maintained.

SP has therefore taken on the task of finding out a great deal more about gossypol (which is made more difficult by the fact that the Chinese have given up experimenting with male pills for the time being),and is also working on other similar possibilities.

On the subject of female contraception work never stops. One method which SP is now exploring is the vaginal ring. It is not a new idea, but this version of it is impregnated with a chemical which prevents conception and remains effective for about a year. It is simple and inexpensive, and having been tried out on monkeys it is now being tried out on women volunteers. If it works, general distribution will follow.

The ring – Dr B explained – is better than the pill. It is not taken by mouth and cannot possibly harm the liver.

They are also experimenting further with the IUD – which stands for Inter-Uterine Device. The question is debated: which is better, the ring or the IUD. There is one great argument in favour of the ring: it is simpler. A woman can put the ring in herself, the IUD needs professional assistance.

Another line of experiment is a new type of pill for women to be taken once a month, just before menstruation or when menstruation is delayed. Yet another form of contraception is the *menstruation inducer*. This must be taken very soon after conception – not later than four days after it – and the drug will often induce menstruation.

Natural methods have been known to humanity from time immemorial, but they, too, are studied scientifically. The simplest method is abstention during the fertile period. This method is advised by the Roman Catholic Church – with moderate success, particularly in the poorer countries. The common objection to it is this: 'You can when you don't want to and you can't when you want to.'

Jokes apart, it is not always easy for a woman to know when her safe period occurs. It seems – perhaps not surprisingly – that primitive women are on the whole much better at knowing their cycles than sophisticated ones. They commit fewer mistakes. The fertile period of a women is only eight to nine days between periods. But this, if you add three or four days of actual menstruation to it, is more than one third of a month – one third of adult life – and for many people there is nothing 'only' about it.

One of the oldest systems, and perhaps the only absolutely safe one, is the lemonade method. This was sometimes recommended by Central European doctors before the war. 'What sort of lemonade?' asked the surprised female patient. 'Just ordinary lemonade. Not too much sugar in it.' – 'And is it really absolutely safe?' the incredulous questioner went on. 'Guaranteed.' – 'And do you take it before or after?' – '*Instead*, my dear. Instead.'

SP (and others) are also trying to develop a dipstick. This is a simple and clever idea. The dipstick will help to discover the safe period – it changes its colour if the period is still unsafe. This, however, is not the most promising line of research. The dipstick is not too reliable as yet, and it is expensive.

SP is also engaged in monitoring the safety and reliability of the various contraceptive methods in use. Women volunteers are being regularly checked all over the world. Some of them take the pill, others are on IUD, or use the ring, or other methods. Effectiveness is being checked and also long-term side-effects, particularly susceptibility to certain diseases. Evidence is contra-dictory and a lot more research is needed. And this takes time. Annual budget or not, the development of a successful contraceptive method takes from fifteen to eighteen years. The new type of vaginal ring was first tested in 1972, and today – in 1986 – it is still in the experimental stage.

The latest experiment is the Norplant Rod. Six of these are inserted in the female body. Dr B remarked: 'This is not our method but it seems to be a good and effective one.' It is a new idea and WHO is monitoring its progress. The rods produce temporary sterility. WHO is trying to perfect the method in two ways: (1) to make *one* rod sufficient instead of using six; (2) to use dissolving rods, which disappear after a certain time and do not have to be taken out.

In dealing with methods of contraception, SP has to face moral objections in addition to problems of money and time. Nobody is *for* smallpox, but many people are *for* uncontrolled conception and therefore against the use of any kind of contraceptive. It can be pointed out that he who is against contraception is also against the prosperous future – perhaps the survival – of the human race, and *for* famine and starvation in many parts of the world. But it remains impossible lightly to dismiss the moral views of very many sincere individuals, and of many equally sincere and far more powerful institutions.

The Greatest Threat

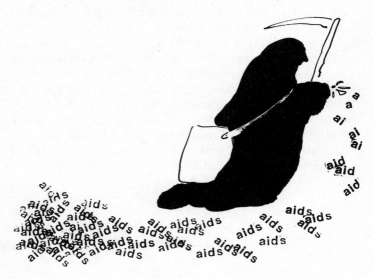

When I first visited WHO's headquarters, the threat of AIDS was fairly new. Some of the high-ups grumbled about the publicity given to AIDS. It affected only a tiny fraction of the population – so it was then believed – yet all the papers, medical and general, were full of it and immense sums of money were being given to AIDS research while much more wide-spread diseases – heart-trouble of various kinds, cancer, kidney and liver ailments etc – were starved of funds.

At that time my heart – if not my head – was with the grumblers. If you are given a vast and important task, carrying on a global fight such as against heart-disease or cholera, then that has to be the most important matter for you and, yes, you *should* be jealous of anything that also needs money, time and brains. You *should* be biased in favour of your own task. There are arbiters in high places – wise and experienced men or faceless bureaucrats or a mixture of the two – and it is up to them to strike a just balance; or not, as the case may be.

Many of those early dissenters must have changed their views by now. People with heart-trouble or cancer still vastly outnumber AIDS-sufferers, but the number of AIDS cases is increasing alarmingly. Every child knows the story of chess and the Shah of Persia. For the sake of those few people who may not have heard it – if they really exist – I shall repeat it here very briefly. The inventor of chess in the fifteenth century took it to the Shah, who was delighted with the new game. The Shah graciously agreed that the game be named after him: *chess* is the same word as *shah*, and the ruler meant to reward the inventor generously. He could choose any reward he wanted, but he was a modest chap and asked only for some grains of wheat. One single grain should be put on square one of the chess-board, and the number of grains should be doubled for all the subsequent squares, up to sixty-four. The Shah thought that this wish was ridiculously modest, but if that was all the man wanted, so be it. The Shah's servants brought out a sack of wheat from the royal granaries and started putting individual grains on the squares. They were surprised to see that one sack was not sufficient, so they brought out another. Soon enough all the granaries of Persia were emptied but all the wheat of the country was not enough to pay the inventor. So, as the second best thing, the Shah ordered that the inventor be beheaded for asking for something that the Shah could not fulfil.

It is not clear yet who will be beheaded in this case, but it seems alarmingly clear that Aids is spreading almost at the speed of the multiplying grains.

In Britain the figures are still comparatively low in absolute numbers although here, too, they are worrying enough. In May 1986 a government institution (the Communicable Diseases Surveillance Centre) reported that there were 184 cases in Britain in 1985 and they expected 336 new cases in 1986. By the end of May 1986 – less than half of the year – these expectations were exceeded: there were 367 new cases and the total – according to new estimates – will reach 700 new cases in 1986 i.e. almost double of the original forecast. But even the previous, more optimistic, forecast was not all that reassuring. They expected 785 cases for 1987 and 1847 new cases for 1988. The figures are not only optimistic, they are also misleading. British experts now maintain that, in fact, at least 20,000 people are infected with the virus, of whom about 14-15 per cent (about 3,000 persons) will develop the full illness. Even so, British and European doctors hope that the great advantage over the Americans will work in their favour. It took three years for AIDS to cross the Atlantic from the US – or more precisely: to recross the Atlantic, as it is supposed to have originated in Africa.

The situation in the US is more alarming.

The Times reported from Washington (14 June,1986) that the number of AIDS victims would increase to more than tenfold in the next five years. They expect 270,000 cases and 170,000 deaths by 1991. By then 54,000 people will have died each year as a result of the disease, more than the numbers killed on American roads.

But the situation is, in fact, even worse than that. According to American health officials more than a million and a half people are already infected with AIDS. They are all ill themselves, or are at least potential carriers. About 20 or 30 per cent of these people will develop the full disease within the next five years. 'AIDS will become one of the nation's killers, ahead of deaths from pneumonia and influenza, car accidents, diabetes, suicide, liver diseases and hardening of the arteries.'

AIDS (Acquired Immune Deficiency Syndrome) was not taken too seriously to start with by quite a number of scientists who should have known better. A number of medical gentlemen believed that it was caught only by active and particularly promiscuous male homosexuals. The attitudes of medical gentlemen towards this group have always varied but whatever they thought of them they agreed – rightly – that they were, after all, only a small minority of the population. While it remains true that the most frequent way of transmitting AIDS is anal intercourse, it was discovered soon enough that there were other ways of transmitting it. In 1981 the homosexuals of New York and San Francisco were, undoubtedly, the most exposed communities. Then new threatened groups were discovered. There are some African countries where AIDS is a heterosexual disease and about half of its victims are women. Contact with African prostitutes may have been the original means by which the disease was introduced to the United States. Heterosexual contact with infected people caused the spreading of the disease, and soon enough two further dangergroups were discovered: drug-addicts, sharing infected syringes, and hospital patients who received transfusions of infected blood.

No one knew how fast and how wide the disease would spread and prediction was extremely difficult because those who are visibly ill with AIDS are only the tip of the iceberg. For every fatally ill victim there are five (and according to some estimates ten) others whose infection is less severe and who have a good chance of surviving. But in addition to these people (fatalities and less severe cases) there are fifty (and perhaps even a hundred) *per person* who are also infected but show no symptoms of the disease and feel that they are in perfect health. These people can infect others, and their number was estimated to be well over a million in the United States, a year ago.

WHO has thrown itself into the fight with great determination. But WHO – and others – are very far from a breakthrough. Researchers hope to find some preventive medicine in three to five years but, at the moment, there seems to be little hope of cure for those who are already suffering from AIDS. The main target of AIDS is the white blood-cells (known as T74 lympho-cytes) – indispensable elements of the body's system of immunity. AIDS sufferers remain exposed to all sorts of infections with which a normal boday can deal, and also to various forms of cancer. This was known from the beginning. Now it is also known that the disease may attack the brain cells – even the brain cells of unborn babies – and the eyes and eyelids. And while intercourse and blood infusion remain the commonest means of infection, the virus has also been discovered in saliva, urine and tears.

It was in 1978 that AIDS cases were first discovered in the West (in Los Angeles), and in 1981 it was acknow-ledged as a threat and an epidemic. Was it a new disease? Or did it exist – asked the Americans – at other places in other forms? It is thought, though not generally accepted, that AIDS is, in fact, a new disease and that the AIDS virus originated in Central Africa in the 1960s. The virus is supposed to have mutated from one found in monkeys.

Monkeys are made to pay for this. They are used for experiments, infected with AIDS, tortured and killed. Yes, yes, of course, it is very important for the human race, we must prefer humans to monkeys and all that sort of thing. I quite agree. Yet: poor monkeys.

This AIDS problem has another nasty undertone. Morality sooner or later rears its ugly head everywhere, and often nothing is more immoral than morality. Quite a few people said this: AIDS being the disease of male homosexuals, it serves them right. They deserve God's punishment for their wicked ways. Poor God, He is often attributed nasty motives by the Faithful and He cannot (or at least does not) protest. This attitude is pretty mediaeval. Although it has become clear that hetero-sexuals and women, perfectly asexual drug-takers and babies are also threatened, this 'God's-just-punishment' murmur is still audible from certain quarters. It should be remembered that some among an earlier generation of medicos and moralists were dead against the treatment of *all* venereal diseases. These diseases, they said, were God's just punishment for immorality, so it was a sin to interfere with His will. Today, when we hear of those medical men declaring that it was a sin to treat the sick, and a considerable part of priggish society agreeing with them, many of us feel outraged. But when the same attitude is repeated in a slightly different form, in slightly different circumstances, many of us fall into just the same kind of attitude.

I have no particularly soft spot for homosexuals – among other things, I have never understood why they call themselves *gay*. On the whole they are a self-conscious and humourless lot. *Lug* – short for lugubrious – would be a more fitting name for them. But whether I like them or not, and whether they call themselves gays or lugs, is neither here nor there. To call them wicked is even sillier than to call them gay. Not one of them has ever sat down to make the choice: 'Should I be a nice, decent heterosexual (molester of little girls, perhaps) or should I become a wicked and terrible homosexual?' As no man has ever chosen to become black instead of white or vice versa, or to have blue eyes instead of brown ones, so no one has ever decided to become a homosexual. (But we don't all have to love people with blue eyes.)

It is ridiculous that such arguments are being called for in the last few years of the twentieth century. You do not treat sick people because they are good or bad; you treat them because they are ill. You do not feed starving people because they are decent, God-fearing folk of the right political persuasion; you feed them (that is if you feed them at all) because they are starving. And in this case common humanity is backed up by crude self-interest. Whatever you may think of God's just or unjust punishment, you should treat male homosexuals because otherwise (or even so) you may have to be treated yourself.

The Greatest Triumph

WHO's greatest triumph is the eradication of smallpox.

For young Western man – indeed, for not-so-young Western man, like myself – the word *smallpox* is a distant memory of some bygone, terrible danger. What we remember is this: every two or three years the papers whipped up a slight smallpox scare. In a large port an Asian or African sailor was suspected of being infected by smallpox, he was isolated, all his contacts – as far as possible – were traced, they were isolated and then vaccinated too. The papers tried to keep up the excitement but it always died down in a few days. Modern life is fast, and new sensations are needed.

The issue did not seem to concern 'us'.

People's memory is short. Smallpox used to be a horrible danger, a rival of the even more horrible plague, and not so very long ago it threatened us all. At the beginning of the twentieth century smallpox affected every continent and every country in the world. The last serious outbreak in Britain occurred in 1903. During the first half of the present century smallpox was eliminated from most countries in Europe, North America and Oceania, but it remained a dreaded threat and mass killer in Asia, Africa and South America.

WHO was established in 1945 and it was thirteen years later that they made the great decision: smallpox must be eradicated. During the subsequent decade they made great progress: another twenty-eight countries became free of the disease. Yet it remained endemic in thirty-three countries with a total population of 1,200 million and – even after this partially successful fight – 10-12 million people were infected and more than two million died every year.

While AIDS seems to be a completely new disease, smallpox is one of the oldest plagues of humanity. Macaulay described it as 'the most terrible of all the ministers of death'. Epidemics frequently swept across the world, killing millions, decimating huge populations and, indeed, altering the course of history. It was Edward Jenner, an English West-country doctor, who discovered (well, not quite, see later) that vaccination with cowpox would protect people against smallpox. Jenner's idea was accepted, millions of people were inoculated and many millions saved; yet, more than 170 years later smallpox was still raging in many parts of the world.

It is not known where smallpox first appeared. It is believed that one of the pox-viruses of animals gradually affected man. But all this happened very long ago. It seems probable that smallpox occurred in China, or the Indus Valley, and in North Africa about 10,000 BC. The first known smallpox victim is Ramses V, Pharaoh of Egypt, or to give him his full titles: Live Horus, Mighty Bull, Repulser of Millions, Sovereign Protector of Egypt, Pharaoh of Upper and Lower Egypt, Lord of the Two Lands, Son of Re. Ramses V died in 1157 BC of an acute illness, at the age of forty. His mummy bore evidence of a rash which indicated smallpox. The mummy was discovered in 1898 and is now in a Cairo museum. As it is one of the best preserved mummies, the museum authorities, naturally enough, refused to let the American Donald Hopkins and his fellow-academics cut out a piece of skin or otherwise mess about with it. However, they were able to collect tiny particles of skin from the shroud. Dr Hopkins concludes his report: 'Despite the limited areas accessible for inspection, the rash is quite striking and is remarkably similar to smallpox.' Hopkins and company could not cut out enough skin to find pox-virus, so they cannot be absolutely certain that their evidence is conclusive. But Dr Hopkins is confident: '...after seeing at first hand the rash on this remarkable mummy I am almost as convinced that he did indeed have smallpox as if I had actually seen a 3000 year-old pox virus.'

By the eighth century AD smallpox epidemics were raging in Europe and the disease had spread from China to Japan. Arab armies carried it across North Africa. It also spread south of the Sahara, but Southern Africa was miraculously spared until the early eighteenth century when ships brought it to Capetown from India. Even Iceland was not spared: the disease reached it in the fourteenth century and from there it spread to Greenland.

It spread on and on. It reached the Caribbean Islands in the sixteenth century and killed more than three million people in the Aztec Empire of Mexico. The Peruvian Empire was 2,000 miles south of Mexico but the disease got there too five years later. North America was spared for some time. Smallpox reached the American mainland at Massachusetts early in the seventeenth century.

I said earlier that smallpox had influenced the course of history. This is no exaggeration. WHO published a booklet in 1980 called 'The Global Eradication of Smallpox'. It says:

'In the course of its lethal wanderings smallpox exercised enormous influence on human affairs. In Asia it killed Emperors of China and Japan and disrupted wars in colonial Ceylon. Prayers for relief were made to goddesses of smallpox in Africa, China and India. Following the death of the Chinese emperor from smallpox, one of his sons was elected as the new emperor expressly because he had already had the disease. Yoruba-speaking people in West Africa worshipped a god of smallpox. In Africa it killed two kings of Dahomey and devastated the Hottentot tribe in Southern Africa. In Europe smallpox killed five reigning monarchs in the eighteenth century alone, ended the English royal house of Stuart, shifted the Austrian Habsburg line of succession four times in as many generations, and caused a violent pandemic after the Franco-Prussian War of 1871. The disease killed an estimated 400,000 Europeans a year and caused over a third of all the blindness of the eighteenth century. In the Americas smallpox facilitated the European conquest and colonization by decimating native American populations. It also prevented an American army from capturing Canada in 1776.'

The book also speaks of the connection between smallpox and religion:

'Smallpox and religion were interwoven in many ways. Smallpox was first introduced into Japan from China with Buddhism, carried across North

Africa with Islamic armies, and reintroduced into Europe by returning Crusaders. Fear of the disease is said to have been a significant force in encouraging the early growth of Christianity just as scarring from smallpox sent many medieval European girls and women into nunneries. In parts of Africa burial rites for victims were responsible for spreading the disease among mourners.'

Modern as well as ancient medical men were, of course, desperate to find a treatment for smallpox. They all failed. Many curious ideas became fashionable from time to time but they were useless. One of the most curious emanated from Japan in the tenth century. It was alleged – and seriously believed – that red-coloured objects cured smallpox. This belief persisted and treatment with red light was carried out in Europe and North America even in the twentieth century. The idea that red cures everything has persisted in other fields to this very day.

Prevention, however, proved to be much more successful. Variolation (this is the medical term for smallpox-inoculation, deriving from *variola* which means smallpox) reached Europe and North America in 1721, but it had been practised in China, India and some parts of Africa for centuries.

The idea was simple: inoculation infected people with a less severe form of the illness than that caught in the usual way from other people through the respiratory organs. In ancient India Brahmin priests travelled through the country, praying to the Goddess of Smallpox and, at the same time, inoculating as many persons as they could. The Chinese practised inoculation in the eleventh century and according to some historians even much earlier than that. It was in 1721 that Lady Mary Wortley Montagu, wife of the British Ambassador to Turkey, observed the practice in Constantinople and decided to persuade the English to follow the Eastern example. It was in the same year that the practice reached North America, too, once again through the good services of a non-medical person. The Rev Cotton Mather learnt about it in Africa and introduced it in Boston.

Edward Jenner, an English country doctor, appeared on the scene two generations later. His discovery was not revolutionary, but his impact was. Jenner himself modestly disclaimed any originality for his discovery. He said that two decades before his discovery he heard a Dorset girl declare that she could not be infected with smallpox since she had already had the cowpox. This belief, added Jenner, was widespread in England. During the epidemic in 1774 a Dorset cattle-breeder, Benjamin Jesty, inoculated his wife and two sons with cowpox. Many people accused him of killing his family but, in fact, he saved them all.

Jenner followed the same practice. His great merit was not that he inoculated a large number of local people but that he *proved* that these people became immune to smallpox. The method of proof was dramatic: Dr Jenner infected people with smallpox and they failed to catch the disease. He also proved that cowpox could be transferred from one person to another by inoculation. He administered his first vaccination with cowpox on the 14th May 1796. Two years later he published a pamphlet which caused a sensation in medical circles and was translated into many languages. Jenner foretold that vaccination could eradicate smallpox from the earth. Country after country made smallpox vaccination compulsory and Jenner's forecast proved to be correct: a few decades later the disease almost completely disappeared from many countries. It remained, however, a savage killer in others.

WHO's campaign was based on a simple idea: at least 80 per cent of whole populations had to be vaccinated and a hundred per cent whenever possible. This intensified programme began in 1967. At that time forty-six countries recorded 131,697 cases but this number was, in fact, misleading, not more than one per cent of the true number of cases. A major reservoir of smallpox was Africa, mostly south of the Sahara, but there were numerous cases also in Asia – mostly in India, Pakistan, Bangladesh, Nepal and Afghanistan, as well as Indonesia and Brazil.

I do not intend to go into the details of the campaign. The invention and use of bifurcated needles and the difficulties of obtaining reliable data are complicated side issues. The campaign, however, in spite of many difficulties, was an astonishing success. Smallpox was eradicated from twenty countries in three-and-a-half years. Brazil's last case was detected in 1981 and Indonesia's a year later. By the summer of 1973 the transmission of smallpox was interrupted throughout the whole of Africa, except in Ethiopia.

If Ramses V, Pharaoh of Egypt, is the first known smallpox victim – who is the last? This question is an easy one: the last man to catch smallpox was Ali Maow Maalin, a twenty-three year old labourer from Merka, Somalia. Merka is a busy little seaport with a population of 30,000. Maalin fell ill and the first diagnosis was malaria. On the 27th October 1977 he developed rashes and after that there was no doubt about the real nature of his illness.

The last smallpox drama began in the usual way: the escape of the virus had to be stopped. All possible contacts of Ali Maow Maalin – 161 people altogether – were traced, isolated and vaccinated. Dr A. Deria of Mogadishu writes: 'At the hospital a tight ring of quarantine and vaccination was set up, covering all staff and patients. Warning signs were put up, and a 24-hour police-guard was posted at the hospital entrance.' There was, one day, a great scare: two nurses fell ill and three others, described as 'neighbourhood contacts' also showed alarming symptoms. They were all isolated but developed no rashes and, in fact, they were suffering

from some other illness. All of them recovered. So did Ali
Maow Maalin.

*

It is extremely difficult to state with certainty that a
disease has been totally eradicated. So a Global Commission was established to investigate these claims. It
met in 1978 and again in December 1979. Its report
stated:

1. Smallpox eradication has been achieved throughout the world.
2. There is no evidence that smallpox will return as
   an epidemic disease.

So what should happen about smallpox vaccination? –
introduced as compulsory in most countries of the world
after defeating strong resistance. Obviously, it is no
longer necessary. In fact, it is pointless. The Global
Commission declared that as smallpox has disappeared,
smallpox vaccination might as well disappear, too. The
report goes on: 'Because vaccination may result in
serious complications, which are occasionally fatal, no
one except investigators should be vaccinated in any
country *including those where monkeypox has occurred.'* (My
emphasis.)

In days of old, when the agitation was *for* vaccination,
we were not told about the possibility of the fatal dangers
of vaccination, but this may be regarded as a matter of
the past.

More timely is the question of monkeypox. Monkeypox remains the last question-mark about the eradication of smallpox, but it is a tiny question-mark and
means no real world-wide danger.

Scientists were obviously worried: was there a hidden
reservoir of viruses which might bring the disease back?

For a while monkeypox seemed to be the only danger but, in fact, it is not. The virus is quite different from the variola-virus; the disease itself is much milder than smallpox; and there is no danger of a monkeypox epidemic among the human population.

So we can declare – and the Global Commission has declared – with a great deal of confidence, amounting to certainty, that SMALLPOX IS DEAD.

WHO may be proud of its leading part in the campaign. But the organisation does not rest on its laurels. I talked about the eradication of smallpox with one of the WHO bosses who is engaged in population – that means over-population – problems. He remarked that, in the long run, over-population was a graver danger than any infectious disease. He, too, acknowledged WHO's great success in the smallpox campaign, but added with a wry smile:

'Nobody is *for* smallpox. But not everybody is for contraception.'

PART THREE
KENYA

Looking Around

It was suggested at WHO that I ought to see one of their *field-operations*, and after a great deal of thought Kenya was suggested for this purpose.

On approaching Nairobi airport, I recalled how little I knew of Africa. I had visited, and written about, the four other continents plus a number of Pacific Islands and other odd places, but I had never written a word on Africa. I had set foot on African soil only twice in my life, on both occasions in Dakar, the capital of Senegal. On the first occasion I went only for dinner. This sounds grand. To drop in somewhere in West Africa just for a snack is high life. The truth suggests a little lower life. We – i.e. about sixty English and eight French writers – were on our way to Rio de Janeiro for a PEN Club conference in 1957 and landed in Dakar to refuel both the plane and ourselves. We were received kindly, indeed ceremoniously, by the Senegal PEN. There were speeches, a good meal and atrocious Algerian wine. A few of our French colleagues were so outraged by the quality of the wine that they decided then and there that Algeria should be given up. Soon it was. After a two or three hours stop we boarded our plane again and off we flew. Next morning we had to get up at five o'clock, all of us hungry, sleepy, irritable and petulant; nevertheless we, the English contingent, watched the French with amazement: all the Frenchmen – bending and stretching and squatting – shook hands with all the other French-men, ignoring all the English.

On the second occasion I was flying home from Brazil in 1975 and decided that I ought to get more out of Africa than just a sniff at the airport. I did, but not much more. I spent a few days in Dakar, talked to a number of people – politicians, writers, film-makers, businessmen – but as I spent most of my time on the beach of my hotel, I still cannot call myself a real expert on Africa.

Quite a few Westerners try to be honest in their attitudes to Africa and to black people generally, but not many of them – of us – succeed. A surprising number retain a condescending, even contemptuous attitude; a lot would have nothing to do with Africa if it weren't that they make money out of it (a fact which, of course, they do their best to conceal); and some swing to the opposite extreme, moved by guilt for their past attitudes or for those of their ancestors, and appear to feel that no black man can do any wrong – which is, of course, as condescending as open contempt. I always suspect vociferous and uncritical admirers of black people: they are often fighting their own concealed and perhaps unconscious racism. The truth is that some black people are likeable, some detestable, and most just middling – just like white and yellow and brown people. Even black politicians basically resemble other kinds, some of them being decent men who are trying to do their best for their nations, and others corrupt pocket caesars. But the countries they are running have been produced by a history unlike that of Europe, and it would be foolish to deny that – just as it is plainly foolish to claim that Africa has done as much for the progress of humanity as Europe has done. Our past is there for the seeing. What should concern all of us now is Africa's future.

When I arrived in Kenya I did not imagine (any more than I had done on my second visit to Senegal) that I was going to learn a lot about Africa. I simply felt that to see a little with my own eyes would be better than seeing nothing.

If you are searching for Evelyn Waugh's Africa you will be disappointed with Nairobi airport. It could be any of the smaller international air terminals in Europe. It is most efficiently run. The immigration officer was neither courteous nor discourteous, he was just a professional who worked fast and without fuss. For a moment, when I changed some money into Kenyan shillings, I thought I had been diddled, but this turned out to be the result, not of paranoia (I don't suffer too badly from that), but of my poor eyesight, and luckily I realised the fact before I opened my mouth to complain.

In the hotel everyone was friendly and efficient, completely without the hardly-concealed hostility, or else servility, which you sometimes meet in the West Indies. You do not find a Jamaican-type apartheid in Kenya either: in Jamaica's expensive restaurants and luxury hotels *all* the guests are white and *all* the waiters, dishwashers and sweepers are black. Not here. You see many black customers, many white waiters and some white dishwashers. I know that long years of rancour, hatred, oppression and violence do not disappear at a stroke but they are not noticeable on a superficial level.

Technical matters are a different story: it does not take long to discover that hardly anything works in Kenya.

95

The telephone is bound to be your first disappointing encounter. The operator is kind and helpful and she tries hard. But to get through is an uphill struggle. I had a radio in my room but it did not work. I called the porter who sent up a mechanic. He examined the radio with expert eyes and then declared: 'It does not seem to be working.' After that he left, never to return.

The lift refused to go up to my floor, the second, but had no objection to the third. So I had to walk one floor down on arrival and two floors down on departure – no great hardship but unusual in an international luxury hotel. The most mysterious phenomenon was the plug in my washbasin. When I pulled it out, the water did not move, it just stayed in the basin, but when I put it back, the water gurgled out at a high speed.

I was told by residents, who know them well, that Kenyans learn all technical matters, innovations and inventions quickly. They are good at handling things – even very complicated things – as long as they work. But if something breaks down they rarely know how to repair it, and are lost.

About things not working we, in England, have the same attitude towards Kenya as Americans have to England. Quite a pleasant, green country, they say, but nothing works there. To the Americans we smugly reply: one should not judge a country by its lifts, telephones and plugs; to the Kenyans we say: that's all very well, but things *should* work.

The more you learn of 'them', the more you learn of yourself. They seem to be a friendly and relaxed people, yet from newspaper reports appearing every day, as well as from talk with local people, you hear about robberies, muggings, and quite unnecessary, vicious violence. You shake your head, but soon enough you realise that 'they' are really 'us'. Indeed, our own savages, terrorists, fanatics, criminals and desperate drug-addicts are probably worse. As I have mentioned, I found the Kenyans polite and considerate. The one thing that surprised and disturbed me was that they were much more courteous to me than to one another. I would be waiting in a post office queue. The official would be incredibly curt, if not downright rude, to his compatriot ahead of me. Having dismissed him in a most unceremonious manner, he would turn to me with perfect courtesy.

Kenya is a one-party state, KANU, the Kenya African National Union, founded by President Kenyatta, being the party. Nevertheless, Kenya has a vague kind of democracy: voters can choose between personalities. The excuse for the one-party system is that the country is 'not ready yet for democracy'. Is there any country which is really ready for democracy? And, indeed, is there any country which is not? Democracy, among other things, means to be allowed to make your own mistakes. Sometimes people make the right choice, sometimes they make a foolish choice. But if they have a chance to choose, they can blame no one else but themselves. (Of course, they *do* blame everybody else, first of all the government they have chosen.) The other justification put forward is that the President knows best. President Kenyatta's shadow hangs heavily over Kenya and his successor.

All things considered, life is reasonably free, there are no plots, the President is safe, conditions are stable. President Moi is not worshipped – there is no *Maoism* in Kenya, or Zaire-type *Mobutism* – but his picture is pretty ubiquitous and he is built up as a very wise and practically omniscient person. When I was there, President Moi made a speech about traffic accidents, demanding more care on the roads and said, for example: if people were driving more carefully there would be fewer accidents. So people were admonished and everyone went on driving as before. The press repeatedly quoted the President's words as pearls of wisdom. If accident figures happened to go down soon after that speech, it will have been a consequence of Moi's wise warning; if they happened to go up, it will have been because a thoughtless and ungrateful population failed to heed the President's wise warning. He can't lose.

*

One has often heard the verdict that Kenya is Africa's success-story. I am not in a position to compare Kenya with other African states, not even with Senegal, but it seems evident that while Uganda, Nigeria and Ghana used to be equally pleasant and peaceful places, they are not so any more. Uganda has sunk to the lowest level of the three mentioned: indeed, Kenya shelters many thousands of Ugandan refugees.

What is the explanation for Kenya's success?

1. The first secret seems to be tolerance – not that Kenyan society is all that tolerant, but it is the most tolerant in Africa. While Britain is becoming more and more restless, uncertain of herself, violent and less tolerant, Kenya slowly gains confidence and is settling down. This new tolerance manifests itself in several ways. Tribe is still important, as it is everywhere in Africa, but it is not an overwhelming, all-dominating issue. President Moi, unlike Kenyatta, is not a Kikuyu, he comes from a smaller tribe from the centre. This fact calms the Kikuyu's rivals and although it creates a feeling of uneasiness in the Kikuyu, tribal strife and discord is not a dominating problem in Kenya just now.

2. Kenya has a middle class. It is only a budding middle class – although there are a number of very rich people in the country – but the influence of it is very great. The middle class is imitated everywhere, it lays down the rules for morals, ambitions, manners and fashion. The middle class is not closed, you can easily slip into or out of it. It is, in fact, not so much a class in the old, even Victorian, sense of the word, as a way of life. This simple truth reflects the failure of Karl Marx. It is not the capitalist state that withers away, but the proletariat,

98

and its withering away is a good thing – a very good thing for the proletariat itself. It is the success of the working class that kills the proletariat and assures, in many countries, a decent life with good wages for working people. (Of course, I am aware that many problems and difficulties remain, but I cannot go into details. I am not writing an essay on economics, I am painting with a broad brush.) In our own chiefly middle-class country people – even many of the unemployed – have television and video sets, bathrooms, some sort of private transport and holidays abroad – a far cry from the squalor of the industrial revolution. But a true Marxist cannot tolerate such improvements. Without a proletariat, poverty and squalor, no revolution will ever break out. But what is revolution for? Marxist revolution could nowhere achieve the well-being which the rotten capitalist system has been seen to achieve without a revolution – at least without a shooting revolution.

Kenya is still far from being a middle-class nation, but middle-class morals, manners and aspirations are gaining ground and exercise a growing influence.

3. Indians form an essential part of this middle class. All societies need Jews, in the nasty mediaeval (and modern) sense of the word, and Kenya is no exception. The story is always the same everywhere. A group of foreign immigrants, or people of foreign ancestry, or even a native group that follows a new religion or some other new creed, is regarded with suspicion. In times of economic, political or some other kind of crisis this suspicion becomes maniacal hatred. The group is never fully accepted and is denied certain jobs, positions, dignities, so its members are determined to prove themselves and work harder than ever. This push leads to success and success is, as a rule, a much more dangerous matter than failure. It is bitterly resented by the duller and lazier layer of the native population. The natives try to convince themselves and their compatriots that the

minority group's success is not due to hard work, let alone to superiority, but has been won by trickery, cunning and dishonesty. In times of economic or political crisis the suspicion grows into hatred and governments are often only too willing to fan the flames and find a scapegoat for their own failure. The newcomers, the strangers, the immigrants – in other words: the *Jews* – on the other hand are, of course, unable and unwilling to accept this interpretation. They do believe in their own superiority and the worse the persecution, the stronger this belief becomes. They have been excluded from certain professions, so they crowd into others and dominate them. They get more than their 'fair share'. These iniquities, persecution, self-defence and a wrong social or economic balance lead to tension, bitterness, revolts, massacres, pogroms and holocausts.

This is the essential story of the Armenians in Turkey (ending in hideous massacres), the Huguenots in France (culminating in St Bartholomew's Night) and the Moriscos (Christians of Moorish origins, culiminating in their mass expulsion from Spain). The list is interminable, from ancient times till today's civil war between Tamils and Sinhalese in Sri Lanka.

There have occurred a few exceptions from this general rule of human behaviour. The Dutch, for example, in the seventeenth century, generously let in large numbers of Jews expelled from Spain and Huguenots fleeing from France. They did not do badly with these newcomers and their generosity brought them rich rewards.

Huguenots, Moriscos, Tamils have always been the ideal Jews. Kenya has a shortage of real Jews (and anyway, after Hitler antisemitic persecution is in temporary decline) so it has to make do with Indians.

The Indian's plight is far from terrible. They are clever, decent, hard-working people and, as is usual, are resented for their success. But, as I have said before, Kenya is a reasonably tolerant society and many Indians reach high office and are held in great esteem. Many Kenyans will vent their passionate dislike of Indians in private conversations. Indians, on the other hand – and also in private – declare they want to leave Kenya. But they are too busy making money and they are enjoying a pleasant life in a pleasant land, so they go on grumbling and stay put.

4. Kenya has solved its black-versus-white relations better than most African countries. Kenya means to be – and is – a proud black country, but some white snobbery survives from colonial times. Kenya does not hate its received language – English – in the same way as, say, Zaïre hates French. Swahili is the country's official language but English is widely spoken and everyone who wants to get on in life must learn it. They do learn it without any ill-feeling, and speak it well. Perhaps the great dividing line between black and white is a sense of humour. Black sense of humour exists of course (I am not speaking of 'black humour'). Kenyans are boisterous, laughing people; but their sense of humour is different from ours. The cynical, dismissive wit of a decadent society is not appreciated by them.

5. Another of Kenya's assets is tourism. The country's scenery is breathtakingly beautiful, its climate (in many parts) pleasant and healthy and its wild life parks are magnificent. Tourism is one of the few great blessings of our age, it allows people to know one another, it destroys old-fashioned, stupid nationalistic prejudices, it keeps people busy preparing for invasion by once-hated nationals who come not – as they once did – with hard bullets, but with hard currency. Kenya leads the way for the few great tourist countries in Africa south of Egypt.

Kenya, all the same, has enormous problems. Since 1979 its economy has been suffering from the low price of coffee and the high price of oil. (Oil prices have fallen lately but are rising again.) Difficulties in agriculture have affected the labour force – most people live in rural areas. Rural poverty drives impoverished peasants to the big centres of population and shanty towns are mushrooming everywhere, with their penury, disease and crime. Manufacturing is healthier and some industries go on expanding (sugar, confectionery, clothing and printing), but this is not an unmitigated blessing. The hope of jobs brings more people to the larger towns and their influx increases the misery of those awesome shanty towns. Kenya's gravest problem, however, is the growth of its population. It grows by 4 per cent every year, which means that the country's population is doubled every twenty years while its GNP stagnates. This spells disaster. The problem is aggravated by a curious fact. The majority of the population are still working on the land and for them children mean riches: extra, cheap manpower. Telling them to have fewer children is telling them to stick to their poverty. Children mean not only wealth, but are a sign of virility, status and rank. That's why so many Kenyan peasants are contemptuous of Christianity: 'Only one son? What sort of God is that?'

This is a thumbnail sketch of a country, a mixture of facts and first impressions. I live in England, a country which used to have (and still has) close connections with Kenya. The relationship between the two countries was not always the happiest but, in the end, it worked out well. Both countries are members of the Commonwealth; they know and understand each other. They are close, yet they are poles apart: two countries, situated on two continents, with different histories, travelling in opposite directions. Britain used to rule the greatest empire the world has ever known but she lost it (in fact, gave it up more or less voluntarily); Britain has lost power, wealth, influence and is resigned at the moment to going down.

So Britain is wise, cynical, experienced and accepts the fact that one's (be that *one* a person, a country or an empire) fortunes are bound to change. But Britain is sure of herself: she has proved herself and she can do it again. Kenya is an ex-colony of Britain, newly independent, the success-story of Africa, eager to rise, eager to prove herself and a little uncertain if she can do it. She is also over-sensitive, suspicious of the rich West yet dependent on it; ambitious and humourless.

This is a land where WHO is warmly welcomed and, at one and the same time, nervously resented.

Field Operation

Almost at once I noticed a curious phenomenon in the newspapers in Kenya. There would be a picture of a group of dignitaries – black cabinet ministers and other high officials – and in the centre there would be a white man, perhaps representing the World Bank or some other financial body, or a member of some UN agency, possible WHO. The caption would list the names of all the Kenyans but would not mention the white man, although he occupied the most prominent place in the photograph. At first I thought this was a slip, but when I saw similar pictures with similiar captions almost every day, I realised that it was not error but policy: a Kenyan folk-custom, in fact.

When you think about it, it is easy to solve this mystery. The white man was there to provide money or some other kind of help. The Kenyan government, like many another, needs to take the money but hates to advertise that need. When the conference is over they can hardly tell the white person to vanish into thin air, but they can turn him into a non-person. As far as they are concerned, he no longer exists: an Orwellian solution, even if it is far from the worst practices foreseen in *1984*.

This in itself is a small matter, amusing but unimportant, but it is a symptom of a grave problem. In a successful developing country, as in all other countries, achievement must be the country's own, the result of its government's skill, foresight and determination. All shortcomings are someone else's. Therefore the generosity of foreigners cannot be a favourite subject. In any case, it is insisted, those foreigners are in honour bound to prevent starvation in the less lucky parts of the world while they are enjoying a life of luxury and, indeed, wasting more food than would be sufficient to feed the starving populations. Besides, the West is desperate to prevent Third World countries from falling into the grasp of the USSR, and this has its price.

The international banks and agencies see things in a slightly different light. Take WHO, for example. Not that people in WHO are anxious to discuss the matter in depth, because it is a delicate subject; but one can discern attitudes and ideas from cautious, even evasive, remarks.

Broadly speaking, there are two schools of thought. One holds that WHO's job is to improve health throughout the world - to make this globe a healthy place by 2,000 – and it does not matter who gets the credit for it. Let the Third World governments gain all the glory while WHO does all the work, and shut up about it. The other school agrees with this to some extent, but adds that WHO does have a budget, after all, so must show results, and to show results they must have those results acknowledged. As one WHO official put it: 'If governments reject our advice and help there is nothing we can do about it. But if they follow our advice and accept our money, we want some recognition.' Another official pointed out that recognition is slowly – very slowly – forthcoming. He had been told by one Third World minister of health, 'We are grateful for the money we get from you, but even more grateful for the ideas.'

The picture is, of course, complicated by the fact that the division of achievement is not so simple. Naturally WHO doesn't really do *all* the good work and the governments don't take all the credit in spite of doing *nothing*. People at WHO readily grant that the organisation makes occasional mistakes and has sometimes wasted its funds on unsuccessful projects; while the Kenyan government, for one, does a very good job in many ways, and achieves good results. Its recognition of WHO's help may be grudging (to say the least of it), but it certainly does not rely on WHO for everything it does in the health field.

All the above is a basic and important aspect of WHO's work in the Third World. The accepted formula is this: 'WHO participates but avoids total involvement.'

Like all good formulas, this is a bit vague, and there have been endless arguments and bickerings about the interpretation of these words. Where does participation end and total involvement begin? When this issue was being discussed at a WHO meeting for the umpteenth time, one of the men present announced that he would tell a fable. Frozen silence greeted this threat, but he was undeterred. As you will see, his fable has a strongly Aesopian flavour.

A hen and a pig were taking a walk together, engaged in amicable conversation. As they were passing a little shack selling refreshments the hen exclaimed: 'Oh look – what a nice notice!'

The pig looked, and read BACON AND EGGS SERVED ALL DAY.

He didn't like it at all, indeed he was quite disgruntled and asked: 'What's nice about that?'

'It's about us, don't you see,' said the hen. 'Bacon and eggs – that's you and me!'

'It's nice for you, perhaps,' said the pig. 'For you it's participation. For me it's total involvement.'

The Kenya National Hospital in Nairobi is a vast complex. The hospital's first building, called at the time the Native Civil Hospital, went up in 1901. In 1908 there were forty-five beds (today there are more than a thousand) and they had 712 in-patients during that year, fewer than they treat in a day nowadays. During the First World War the hospital became a camp for the 5th Kenya Rifles. In 1930 a new modern wing with three hundred beds was added. Extension went on all the time. In 1951 the Ismail Rahimtulla wing was added for Asian patients and the hospital was renamed King George VI Hospital. After independence it was renamed again. 'Since a great deal of work of a national nature was associated to the hospital' – says an official pamphlet – 'it became the Kenya National Hospital. Today hundreds of doctors, nurses, occupational therapists, radiographers, laboratory technicians etc look after thousands of in- and outpatients every day in many wards and departments, the largest among them being surgery, divided into general, orthopaedic, cardiographic, plastic, eye- and neuro-surgery.' I was led through all the departments. The place looks like most hospitals in Britain, except that it is even more crowded, more women carry their children in a bag on the back; and many more people are waiting for their turn lying on the lawn, in the blazing sun.

After that I saw quite a few more hospitals and talked to many doctors, consultants, administrators, Ministry of Health officials and nurses. All the doctors and nurses wanted more and better equipment, all the administrators wanted more space, more money and less spending, and all the nurses and students (almost all resident)

107

wanted better accommodation. Psychiatrists told me that psychiatry is something of a newcomer in Kenya but now, at last, is being taken seriously. Depression used to be regarded as laziness but now depressed patients are given proper treatment.

In Nairobi, and even more in the rural areas, malaria is still a grave problem although it does not get too much publicity nowadays. AIDS is more in the news but malaria is still a dangerous killer.

Talking about the requirements of the various hospitals or the various groups in the hospitals, no one ever mentioned pay. Pay is a taboo subject. There are many taboo subjects. Whenever I asked a slightly tricky question of an administrator, even if it referred to his own hospital, I was told that I must ask the Ministry. WHO was not even mentioned by any one of them. When I uttered the name of WHO an embarrassed silence ensued, and people looked at me as if I had uttered an obscenity. One senior administrator even blushed.

I understood. And if by 1990 *all* the children of the world are immunised and *everybody* on earth has safe drinking water – as it is planned and hoped – I think WHO will nod and will understand too, and (perhaps) it will not mind if all the Third World newspapers write glowing articles eulogising their great leaders for their glorious achievement.

Postcript:
Beware of Success?

Earlier in this book I said that there are no solutions to any problems because every solution brings new problems in its wake. Progress usually means that evils are being replaced by evils; but if the first evils were great and the second ones are lesser, then that, of course, really is progress.

Many beneficial drugs, for example, have disagreeable side-effects, many treatments have horrible consequences, and the old saying that the cure is worse than the illness is often literally true. Or take the recent famine in Ethiopia, that colossal disaster to which the rest of the world responded with such touching (if unusual) generosity. The famine was caused because it hadn't rained for seven years. Then it did rain and the famine seemed to be over ... but the rain brought on another problem, a proliferation of locusts which descended on the new and scanty crops and devoured them, causing yet more starvation. The rain had stopped one famine and started another. And think of the old man about whom I was told by Dr C at WHO. He lived in a tiny overcrowded flat with his brother and two sisters, had to work very hard even in his old age, had very little money, and they all had to use a remote outside lavatory. As it happened he got on very well with his family so he didn't mind the crowding, he loved his work, he had very few needs, and none of them had ever had any other kind of lavatory, so he didn't feel too badly off. Then, unexpectedly, the local authority decided that it must care for this poor old man who was working long after he should have stopped and living in such bad conditions. They can't have been doing wrong in seeing to it that he got his pension and rehousing him in a nice little flat, all to himself, in a new block, but as a result of their care he was miserable. He missed his brother and sisters terribly, he had nothing to do, he found the neighbours noisy, the children rude and the pop music pouring through his windows intolerable. He began to be afraid of muggers and housebreakers, became very paranoid and depressed . . . and before six months were up he was dead.

Now, all those problems caused by solutions are real, but still it would obviously be absurd to argue that sick people should not be treated for their illnesses, that what dry countries need is yet more drought, or that local authorities should never rehouse people.

When it comes to economic problems, solutions which create further problems are terribly easy to find – the importation of cheap labour from poor neighbours, for example. That, in several countries, has appeared at first to be a very good solution. It has meant the lowering of prices of manufactured goods and consequently booming export possibilities for the country importing the labour, while in the countries exporting the labour the unemployment problem has been alleviated and much-needed hard currency has been received, sent back home out of the earnings of the workers who have gone abroad.

But economic conditions are not stable, and it can happen – has happened – that the labour-importing country decides that it no longer wants to employ foreign workers, and anyway never meant them to stay permanently. Therefore they are housed in hastily constructed barracks or in shanty-towns where their health is undermined. They pick up and spread diseases and many of them die although proper medical care could have saved them. They are not allowed to bring their wives or girl-friends into the 'host' country, so they very often catch and spread venereal diseases. So the initial happy situation results in the native population blaming the immigrant workers for being dirty, unhealthy slum-makers, and the immigrant workers feeling deeply cheated and abused, to the point of becoming really hostile to the receiving society. Some of them will turn to robbery and rape, and fear and hatred will be added to the receiving society's contempt, while the many innocent immigrants will feel even more cheated, degraded and exploited. Riots will break out, people will be killed, tension will mount and extremists on either side will make a bad situation worse. International tension will grow between the labourers' country of origin and the country where they live and work, and international blackmail will flourish.

Or take the Aswan Dam, a mighty achievement of which, surely, Egypt should be justly proud. Yes – except that the dam is spreading malaria at an alarming rate, and also another dangerous disease called schisbomaosis (blood in the urine).

Or, to jump to quite a different field, take the British Conservative Party, which at the moment of writing is feeling quite nervous about the next election entirely as a result of its own success. In 1979, when the Party came to power, the country's most dreaded threat was rising

111

inflation at well over 20 per cent, and the Trade Unions seemed to have got quite out of control and to be ruling the country. The Tories, under Mrs Thatcher, tamed the unions and curbed inflation. Nowadays new voters refuse to see the unions as terrifying bogey-men and have forgotten the horrid days of constantly rising prices. If the Tories had been less successful and had only half-defeated the threats instead of doing so well against them, their chances would now be better.

To turn to much wider issues, has not the progress of civilisation itself created the most worrying problems? Looking at it in terms of the lives of individuals, too many people now live in enormous cities and work too much (country-dwellers often work even harder, of course, but under less stress). City dwellers have constantly to fill their lungs with evil fumes, while their ears are bombarded with noise. They are always in a rush, always having to deal with problems. Too many of them resort to tranquillisers – they can't sleep at night and make themselves dopey when they ought to be most wide awake. The more successful they are – the more committed to all this rush and pother – the more inadequate they become as human beings, as husbands and parents. They kill themselves and each other increasingly often in traffic accidents and by drinking too much, more and more of them become drug addicts, take to crime, go mad, die of cancer because of smoking, commit suicide ... Our newspapers and television screens overflow every day with these fruits of our all-conquering and glorious civilisation.

Do these random examples tends to show that the final success of WHO – when and if it comes – will bring the gravest dangers in its wake? Imagine that WHO – with the help of other organisations and some governments – is totally successful in eradicating all disease from this globe: the result would be worse than the resurrection of all the dead, as promised by some religions. The population of the world would increase at a terrifying rate (already, according to many experts, it is presenting us with our gravest problem). More and more people, and older and older people, with the young having to work more and more desperately to keep the old, and economies tottering on every side under the strain ... Will we be reduced to *hoping* that new epochs will create new diseases and start killing humanity off with as yet unimaginable epidemics?

So what is to be done?

The answer is simple.

Let us go on trying to make people all over the world as healthy and happy as possible. Humanity survives by facing dangers with courage – even the dangers of success. We cannot refrain from building great dams, or trying to curb inflation or feed the hungry, simply because if we bring them off these achievements may create new difficulties, any more than we can stop treating sick people because some drugs have had side-effects, or refrain from rehousing slum-dwellers because sometimes an individual would rather stay where he was. WHO will, and must, continue to fight disease and for the general well-being of humanity. And if, finally, we *all* become happy and healthy - well, so be it. We will have to face that danger when it arises. It is a threat which is not, alas, exactly imminent.